NOZZERS
FIRST CLASS

Ray Lambert

ISBN 0-9544519-2-9

Published by: RAYL, 13 Weedswood Road, Chatham, Kent ME5 0QR
Typeset by Richard Lloyd, Reading

Contents

By the same author:

Kent Ex-Boxers Association, 'Comes of Age', 1987

Nozzers, 2003

PROLOGUE

The success of my previous book NOZZERS has encouraged me to continue with the rest of the story. The story of my time spent at HMS Ganges. Such were the positive and many comments that I received from people who had read NOZZERS that I hope this book NOZZERS FIRST CLASS will be a welcome companion.

This time we join the boys as they are rated 'First Class' and have adapted somewhat to the place, now that they have a bit of service under their belts. They still look forward to the day when they can get out of the place for good and that day is a lot closer now than it was last time. Their course is half run and they only have about six months to *freedom.*

Once in a while, as they go about their daily routines, they bring to life a recollection from their early days because some things are imprinted upon their brains forever.

Through the central figure, Ginger, we learn more about Chief Bumble from the Annexe, Mick Southern, Ray Leeward, Daisy, Cyril Jury and, of course, bully-boys Dereham and Sweaty Gillette. The always nasty Leverett and Batchelor appear almost as often as they did at the time and remain as unfriendly as ever.

Unsolicited, but nevertheless welcome, comments decreed that this book should be written. Comments such as:

'You've brought back long forgotten memories.'
'The way you have captured the atmosphere is brilliant.'
'You certainly know how to bring a story to life.'

Plus the often repeated:

'I read NOZZERS from start to finish. I couldn't put it down.'

was enough to convince me that the interest is there. I hope NOZZERS FIRST CLASS gives the same pleasure that I'm pleased to learn NOZZERS did and that, once again, I have captured something of the 'old place'.

I enjoyed writing this sequel and it certainly brought to life memories that have lain dormant for half a century. I can hardly believe it was that long ago.

All the tales, trials and tribulations within these pages are true. The only deviations are where I have enhanced small fragments by turning them into readable prose or where I have clarified an obscure point to make it understandable for the reader. As always, the names have been changed to protect the guilty.

I have enjoyed reliving the past and I sincerely hope readers encounter the same enjoyment as they travel through the following pages.

Ray Lambert, 2004.

ONE

First Class!

What should, probably, have been the high point of the inhabitants of Hawke 49 mess's incarceration came in with a whimper and went downhill from there.

Achieving first class status should have ranked in importance only second to getting out of the place for good. Instead there was nothing.

No formal parade of recognition; no meaningful straight-in-the-eye look and firm handshake; no hearty congratulatory slap on the back; no round of applause; nothing. Not even a 'well-done' speech from the divisional officer – typical Ganges.

First class meant nothing. Possibly it meant something to those that were keeping score. There must have been a list – or progression chart – somewhere. Most likely it would have been hanging on the divisional office wall or in one of the numerous books or bits of paper that they appeared to enjoy being surrounded by.

The boys were never allowed inside the divisional office so they would have no idea who was keeping score or, indeed, if a score was being kept and if so, where the results were kept. There must have been an overall progression chart of some sort because, every once in a while, some luckless individual would get back-classed through having failed, or had not taken, one of the many indefinable tests that seemed to be ongoing continuously, although the boys were not aware of any such tests in the first place.

Being back-classed was a major upheaval and a traumatic experience. It meant being spirited out of your class and mess when no-one else was around and delivered into a class of strangers that had started six weeks later. Anyone unfortunate enough to have that misfortune befall them would have to go through the previous six weeks training all over again with a new class and a new instructor. They would have to finish their entire course with that later class and never see their old mess mates again.

Reasons for being obliged to take that retrograde step could be for having spent some time in the sickbay hospital or simply not being quite up to standard in one of those 'secret' tests.

That's how Ginger figured out that there must be some sort of weekly, or at least monthly, progress reports for every boy in the place. Just the same, there didn't appear to be a point when someone – anyone – said: 'You're first class, now'

3

Quite what they expected – if they expected anything – was never put into words. Suddenly they were first class. It just came upon them. The actual date was December the sixth. Sure enough, they'd been working toward their being rated up ever since that first day in The Main, if only they had realised it. But on that particular day they had other things to occupy their minds. It had been a slowly-but-surely progression with someone keeping score and totting up steps achieved on their way to this momentous occasion.

Their biggest and perhaps their only accolade came on the following Wednesday at the pay parade.

When it was Ginger's turn to approach the Paybob's table someone announced: 'Boy first class Lambert, sir,' and seven shillings and sixpence, by way of three half-crowns, was delivered to the top of his hat that he had placed on the table between them. Seven and sixpence a week instead of five shillings was what being first class meant to Ginger and, he suspected most of the others from 49 mess felt the same.

Suddenly first class was good; it meant extra money!

But being first class didn't bring with it any extra privileges as far as the way they were treated was concerned. There was no little tight smile that would have shown understanding; there was not even the merest inclination of the head by way of a small nod of approval implying: *you're first class now and we recognise that fact.* Apart from the money nothing changed. Everything carried on just as usual.

There may have been some small recognition of their elevated status and that, such as it was, came with the issue of a knife. They had not been given a knife straight away with the rest of their kit. In the Annexe during those first few hectic days when they were busy getting kitted out, they were not aware of a knife or that one was missing. No one was aware that they were short of a vital bit of their kit or that it would be issued at a later date, a few months into their year long course.

Whether the two things – becoming first class and receiving a knife, were connected in some way, or if it was simply coincidence that the two happened at the same time, would remain a mystery.

The first time 61 class had an inkling that a knife would soon be theirs was when PO Jury, their class instructor, met them on the edge of the parade ground, diagonally across from Hawke Division and just around the corner from the main gate.

They were heading for the school block, which was just outside the gate and down to the left, when PO Jury appeared and ordered Daisy, their badge boy, to halt the class. Carrying a brown cardboard box, he strode a few paces forward and ordered them to turn right into line and stand easy. They were facing the boys' NAAFI canteen.

'Right then, stay where you are and sing out when your name is called.'

They were still in the dark but everything became clear as he began calling out names, names that he was reading off the knife handles and tossing them to their new owners.

'Right then,' he said, as the box became empty. 'You've all got a knife now. It's part of your kit. Look after it.'

Apparently he had just returned from the Annexe and that corner is where they met. He had been to pick up the knives for 61 class. Each individual knife had the owners name stamped into the handle with metal letter punches.

'Right then,' he said, addressing Daisy. 'Carry on to your next class instructions.' As he spoke he turned away and marched toward the Petty Officers Mess. They didn't know if he looked back at them or not. They were already on their way and round the corner.

That knife in their pocket, weighed heavy as they marched along but they didn't mind. To them it was as precious as a bar of gold.

Not much was absorbed in the school classroom that day as, without exception, the entire class spent the time admiring their new kit addition, under the desk and out of sight of the schoolie.

Presumably Leverett, the other class instructor, did the same for his class because, as the days activity drew to a close, everyone in Hawke 49 mess were either sitting on their bed deep in thought or gathered in small groups – every single one of them carrying his new possession.

But, strangely enough, once the novelty had worn off, knives were rarely used at Ganges. They were meant to be attached to a lanyard and slung around the waist but as they didn't have a spare lanyard that didn't happen. The boy coxswains in the sailing club, wore theirs over their sea jerseys on boating days and a few 'old-salts' like Doug Raines, who was in the sailing club as a coxswain anyway, would strut about with theirs in full view. But for the vast majority who had been issued with them, knives were consigned to the back of lockers and only saw daylight on kit muster days. But as kit inspections could be called for at the drop of a hat, or at an instructors whim, they were never far from sight or mind.

The novelty of owning a 'seaman's dirk' as they were officially called, although no-one ever used that name, was a short lived love affair and they soon became just another item of kit to be accounted for at all times. On the good side, they didn't require any special care. They needed no cleaning or polishing and that fact alone must have been a first for Ganges.

5

On the other hand, kit inspections were a different story and where cleaning and polishing were paramount. Kit inspections were part of the training syllabus and were scheduled for every other week. Hawke 49 mess always endured theirs on a Wednesday. 61 class on one week and 62 class on the alternate week

As with all Annexe instructors, Chief Bumble had taught them how to lay out their kit and present it, ready for inspection.

Upon joining, everybody was issued with a seamanship manual, a blue covered book about nine and a half inches long and six inches wide. As well as becoming their 'bible' that manual also became a template for standardising their kit for inspection.

Chief Bumble had shown them how to roll each individual article of kit round a bit of cardboard – which had to be exactly the same length as the manual – with the name already stamped and sewn over in red silk, clearly showing in the centre. To keep the parcels together each end was tied with a bit of string called clothes stops, about an inch or so from each end.

With obvious exceptions, everything, immaterial of size, had to be rolled the same. Everything from underpants to overcoats were rolled up in the same manner and, when laid out for inspection, all clothes stops had to be in straight lines with each other.

Chief Bumble had taught them well and they had Leverett and Batchelor to ensure they didn't forget, or let their standards slip.

Ganges boys' kit laid out, using their flat kitbag as a base, was a sight to behold. It was almost a sculpture and wouldn't have looked out of place at the Ideal Home Exhibition or on display at a museum or gallery. But it never would be good enough to please Acting Petty Officer Leverett.

They dreaded the days when he would do the inspection. It was almost a certainty that, as soon as he walked in the mess door, someone's painstakingly laid out masterpiece would get a highly polished boot in amongst it and articles of clothing, that in some cases had taken hours to prepare, would be sent sailing all over the place.

Leverett didn't appear to look for anyone in particular but Doug Raines seemed to be the unlucky one who attracted his attention. To some degree, Doug brought attention upon himself by persisting with his 'old salt' attitude. He wore his hat at a rakish angle that he had perfected, despite being corrected and his years were well in advance of his sixteen summers. He tried very hard to create an old-sea-dog attitude and appearance. He had gone as far as to do a sailing coxswains course in his very limited free time, just so he could wear a slightly different rig on boating days and stand out from the crowd. He had got Leverett's full attention the very first time they had met over in the Annexe, but whatever their differences were then Doug didn't deserve that personal attention. His kit was no different than anyone else.

A few months into their course the Navy, in their wisdom, discontinued the practice of using cardboard and clothes were rolled up without. It made life a lot easier although the finished article didn't look as smart.

Inside each locker was almost like a mini kit inspection because everything had to be laid out and arranged in a certain order, just as if it was ready to be inspected – which, unbeknown to them it almost certainly was. Locker doors had to be left wide open all through the day, when the mess was deserted and the boys were quite sure that Batchelor, their assistant divisional officer, would walk up and down each mess in Hawke Division every day, looking for anything he could find fault with in those lockers.

For their first term or so, they were escorted to the laundry but as time progressed, and Batchelor had newer 'new boy nozzers' to hold his attention, 49 mess acquired the privilege of doing their washing unattended. As they became more settled into their new home, most of their smaller items were washed in the mess bathroom during the late evenings and hung to dry in the airing room, although they had to be removed smartly first thing in the morning.

Their basic work dress of No.8s which consisted of a blue cotton shirt and dark blue cotton trousers had to be changed twice a week and so, naturally, had to be washed twice a week. These were usually done in the laundry because there were drying rails to speed the drying process. Somehow that laundry managed to cater for the boys from eight divisions, with up to ten classes in each division, without ever having a double booking or not having spare drying rails.

There was a patriarch type who looked after the laundry. Ginger never learned his name. He never had occasion to speak to him. He was not intimidating like Chalkie White from their Annexe days. The man hardly ever spoke, or if he did it was just quietly to whomever it was that he was addressing. Most of the time he was nowhere to be seen. His main function was to work the hydro – a kind of large spin dryer that was set into the middle of the floor.

In their early days when they first arrived in Hawke Division, their instructor – usually Leverett – would announce: 'Laundry! Grab your dhobying and fall in outside.' They had been issued with a laundry bag as part of their kit. It resembled a pillowcase except it had a drawstring at the open end. They stuffed everything they could lay their hands on into that laundry bag, just like they were ordered to do during their Annexe days.

But now, with a bit of 'service' under their belts, not one of them carried more than the absolute minimum. They had learned though, through experience, to always have something to wash.

In the past a few foolhardies had mustered with nothing and, when questioned, proudly declared: 'My kit's up to scratch, sir!'

Leverett loved someone to say that. He would stare with those bulging eyes of his, getting red in the face until they all knew he was ready to explode. Then the eruption would come.

'Would you like me to find you something?' he would roar.

That would be enough to have the miscreant scurrying back to his locker to get something, anything, whether it needed washing or not.

They'd had a demonstration once when one of their number had been suicidal enough to stand his ground with Leverett. That was as close as they ever wanted to get and they remembered and learned from the encounter. The lad, a rather smartly turned out chap, stated loudly that his kit was in tiptop condition and stood returning Leverett's stare.

Leverett exploded in a bright red fury and strode loudly and deliberately up the stairs and into the mess, the boy following along a few paces behind. With a sweep of his arm Leverett scooped every bit of kit from that lad's locker and stamped up and down on it, kicking it everywhere.

'Now you've got something that needs washing,' he growled.

They all had that incident imprinted in their memory and in particular, the boy whose kit had received the treatment, and all resolved to carry something on all future laundry sessions.

But now that they had reached first class status they had learned how to wash a bit here and there and iron a bit during odd moments, but if they thought Leverett was in one of his aggressive moods they would play his game and just grab their pyjamas from their bed. Having something to wash kept him happy – and if he was happy, they were all happy.

Although washing and keeping kit in immaculately clean condition at all times was an absolute priority at Ganges, the most frustrating chore by far was ironing.

Ginger never got around to counting how many people there were in his class but, like all other classes in all other messes, they formed three ranks at every muster with something like eight to ten bodies in each rank. Doubling that number, to account for their opposite class made a total of something in the region of fifty boys to a mess – and one iron!

There was one socket on the wall that separated the mess from the airing room and no others anywhere else. So they couldn't have plugged in another one even if someone had brought one back off leave, which of course no-one had.

Everyone in the entire establishment had to iron their No.8 shirt and trousers at least twice a week and worse still, press their blue suit ready for Sunday Divisions, the Ganges big parade of the week.

The bully boys and 'sir's favourites' seemed to commandeer the iron for longer than the average time, which meant that the bulk of them had to stand in line waiting for long periods and then rush their stuff through as quickly as possible to give others a chance. Standing in line had to be done, to protect one's place in the queue but it also meant it gobbled up their free time and there was precious little of that to start with.

Dereham was one of the bullyboy brigade. Or at least he thought he was. He had joined up at the same time as Ginger and travelled down on the same train, on that first day. They had been in Jellicoe Two in the Annexe together and now they were still together in Hawke. Dereham was a strange sort of chap. He wanted to run with the hare and the hounds. It seemed that he didn't have much of a home life and he was lonely.

Adopting an aggressive attitude, he felt, gave him a bit of status. He would show no conscience about intimidating or browbeating some unfortunate in the hope that it would stand him in good stead with his front-runner cronies. Then, the very next day, he would want to be best pals again with no mention of the previous days debacle. Deep down he wanted to be liked.

One of his tricks when using the iron had been to wait for one of his cronies of the moment to arrive with their ironing and, as he finished he would hand the iron to his 'mate' thereby allowing him to jump the queue. This happened several times in the early days and objections were met with the same reply: 'Well, I was saving his place next to me in the queue.'

It was Ginger who figured out an antidote to that one. Without drawing attention to themselves, he recruited about half a dozen others into the scheme. They were to sit on their bed with their ironing yet to be done and as one finished he would call over the next one in the scheme. Others, not actually involved in the fiasco allowed it to happen without complaint because they realised, in the long run, it would put Dereham's nose out of joint. It only worked if Dereham was waiting, but work, it most certainly did. He got the picture.

Another stunt he tried but was also short lived, was to stride to the front of the line of people waiting their turn and shout: 'After you with the iron.'

Objections on that occasion were overruled by: 'Well, you never said *after you wiv the iron'* did yer?'

The second time he tried that one was the last time. A welsh chap who, for a while occupied the next bed to Ginger, was next in line.

Dai was from the north part of Wales and was completely different from Taffy-from-the-valleys. Although they were both dark haired, Taffy had a high-pitched, singsong way of talking while Dai spoke deeper and slower.

At that time they had only been in Hawke Division a couple of weeks and Dai hadn't said very much. He wasn't morose or shy, it was simply that a fair haired country boy and a dark haired Welshman from opposite sides of the country hadn't began to communicate. But Dai became Ginger's hero that day.

As Dereham went to pick up the iron, Dai, in front of the queue and whose turn it was next, grabbed the iron first and banged it down on the top of Dereham's hand. Naturally it was burning hot and luckily, only caught Dereham a glancing blow. But the message was loud and clear. Dereham sported a blister on his thumb and forefinger for a few days and thereafter took his turn in line.

Mick Southern devised a stop-gap method of getting a bit of pressing done during busy periods on the iron. He came up with a way of placing a crease between two pieces of cardboard and then pressing it down over the hot pipes in the airing room. How he got the idea remained a mystery. Or maybe it was something that was passed down through generations of boys over the years. Ganges boys were adept at improvisation – plus this idea really worked. Wherever it originated, 49 mess appreciated it. It saved a lot of arguments over the iron and possible embarrassment at Daily Divisions.

Mick's *'Heath-Robinson'* enterprise worked to some degree on No.8s, providing they were not too wrinkled up to start with. It took a while moving the cardboard down the proposed crease bit by bit but it would provide a crease across the shoulders at the back and one down the trouser legs to an acceptable level, providing they kept out of Leverett and Batchelor's fault finding, prying eyesight.

But it really came into its own with the blue suit. Once the creases had been established in their bell-bottoms, it was simplicity itself to keep them using process *'a la Mick'*. The bits of cardboard were the same length as the horizontal creases and pressure from two hands covered the whole width. Best blue suits were only worn once a week at Sunday Divisions, so an occasional refresher on the pipes was all that was required to keep the creases looking sharp.

Back in the Annexe, Chief Bumble had given them a lecture on how the seven creases in their trousers represented the seven seas. But whether there was any basis in fact for that line of thought was debateable. It seemed more likely that they were there to make stowing them away easier; by concertining the legs in their creases suits took up very little space in the lockers.

Bumble had to keep them entertained somehow during their Annexe period. They were nozzers in every sense of the word in those early days, and allowing them free time would only have been counter productive. Particularly the first couple of days before they were issued with their kit and then waiting for the paint to dry where their name had been stamped on everything.

After that, all their free time – and every other kind of time for that matter – was taken up by sewing over the letters of their name with red silk. The business with the red silk took up all their time when they were not otherwise engaged on the parade ground, or in the laundry, or at meals.

But for those first two days Bumble had to find something to keep them occupied and that's where the lectures on the traditions of the Royal Navy came in. He appeared to enjoy rabbiting on about traditions. Everything was built on tradition, he told them. How the seven creases in the trousers represented the seven seas and how the three stripes on the collar were in honour of historic sea battles. The black silk, which had to be folded into eight while wet and allowed to dry in the folded position, was worn around the neck with a blue suit. He said that was in memory of the death of Horatio Nelson. Then there was the lanyard. No-one could come up with a satisfactory reason for what earthly use that was.

Bumble kept them entertained back in those days with his explanations of naval traditions. They sat, enthralled, visualising swashbuckling sea battles and derring-do on the Spanish Main – whatever that was – as he rambled on. He probably laid it on a bit thick realising that he had their undivided attention but Ginger recalled that he didn't mind in the least. At that stage in their new career he didn't know anyone else in the mess and he was happy to lose himself before the mast with Bumble's naval heroes, whether it was Horatio Nelson, Earl Jellicoe or Errol Flynn for that matter. Sitting still and listening to Bumble waffle on was much better than being on the parade ground or scrubbing the wooden decking of the front passage, which had been his job for the six weeks of their Annexe episode.

Looking back to those half forgotten days he had to concede that Bumble's stories were delivered with lots of atmosphere, although his interpretation

11

seemed a load of old twaddle. The trouser creases were there for practical purposes, as an aid to space saving. The collar stripes were simply decoration, and the silk just finished off the plain front of a uniform – but still no-one could figure out what that lanyard was for.

Even in those very early first few weeks, with their blue suits pressed up, they looked smart. Some ready-to-wear suits fitted better than others but, at that stage they didn't know any different. Most of them were in a uniform for the first time and had pressed their suits with vigour and they wore them with dignity.

It was early May when they joined up. Only the first week in May but it was warm and sunny. Some days it was downright hot, so their introduction to Navy serge wasn't the most pleasant of experiences. It was difficult enough mastering the over-the-head jumper for the first few times without the extra hindrances of collar, silk and lanyard to contend with. But with Bumble's guidance they found things began to come together and, by the time their first Sunday Divisions came around, they were all smartly turned out in their 'best suit'. Their marching may not have been up to much but at least standing still they looked the part, all the way from their blancoed hat to their highly polished boots.

Little did they realise it at the time but what they had considered as perfection, or as near perfection as they could get, was just the tip of the iceberg. As the weeks went by and they moved out of the Annexe, their standards progressively improved. At Ganges, a high standard was considered the norm and was not good enough. Every boy was expected to achieve that norm and improve from there – and improve they did. Petty Officer Jury told them as much. Even Leverett was forced into a reluctant acquiescence. Jury had said that there was still room for improvement and although they were hard pressed to see how, or where, the improvement could come from, if he said so then they were ready to go for it.

Jury knew all aspects of his business but in particular he loved the parade ground. He was the sort of chap that stood out from the crowd and he expected them to be the same. They had had classroom sessions with him and they had periods on the four-inch mounting with the dummy wooden shells. By the time Jury had completed that aspect of their training, each of them could man any position on a four-inch twin mounting and carry out that position's function, without fault.

On the parade ground he was in his element. He appeared to enjoy being out there but even so it was never an ego trip for him. He wanted to teach and, as the routines became more familiar, the boys wanted to learn. Jury was a good teacher and when he shouted it was so that his commands could be clearly heard and understood and, unlike Leverett and Batchelor, never in anger. When he employed his loud 'parade ground' voice it was always with precise parade orders and never the venom that other nearby instructors screamed forth. Close to however, when putting someone straight one-to-one, his quiet slightly sarcastic quips would have the same effect. Jury could make them feel inadequate with a few quiet words, which would leave them wanting to do better next time, rather than rebelling like they would against Leverett's hatred

Jury must have had infinite patience. Although they now felt that they could hold their own against drill squads from any branch of the services and from any country, it hadn't always been the case. Their early attempts left a lot to be desired and, at times he must have despaired.

Ginger had done a bit before, with the army cadets back home, so he knew the basics and had a little bit of a head start. He was amused to see how some of them managed to give themselves quite a clout with their rifle while sloping, presenting and ordering arms – and not only themselves but sometimes the person next to them as well. Particularly when sloping arms a bit on the vigorous side and tossing the rifle right over the shoulder to hit whoever was unfortunate enough to be in the rank behind. Once in a while poetic justice lent a hand with an over enthusiastic order arms resulting in a rifle butt being dropped heavily onto toes.

They struggled and strained but they learned. Despite bruises and cuts – how did anyone cut their fingers? – it began to come together, even when bayonets were introduced. Bayonets changed the balance of the rifle and the movements had to be readjusted to accommodate the extra weight. But apart from an occasional hat being knocked off, due to the extra length of a bayonet not being allowed for and once when a hat was skewered, PO Jury moulded them into a close-knit unit where they reacted as one man.

As one of their number remarked: 'We've gone from confusion to absolute unison.'

As time had progressed and they reached a high standard, POGI Jury was proud of them. Cyril Jury rarely showed any excessive emotion but he was proud of 'his boys' and had trouble disguising that fact. He wasn't a selfish man and they knew his pride was for them and their achievement and not in any way in himself for what he had taught them.

They liked PO Jury from the first time they had met him, when he and Leverett had come over to collect them from the Annexe all those months ago. They quickly learned to respect him and, as time passed, that respect was reciprocated.

In keeping with all Ganges instructors, he wasn't over friendly or familiar with them but at the same time, he never forced them into extra drills or punishment routines simply to satisfy a lust for power. He had power. They knew he had power and, unless they blotted their copybook in some way, he was quite happy not to have to demonstrate that fact.

He had given them his best and they had responded by giving their best. They wanted to please him and they had done exactly that.

Acting Petty Officer Leverett, the seamanship instructor, was a different story altogether. His normal facial features wore a fearsome scowl that made him look aggressive and the boys were very quickly to learn that those features illustrated his demeanour exactly.

His expression rarely altered and his attitude matched that expression. Anyone that had even the slightest doubt had those doubts dispelled forever the moment he opened his mouth. It was most unusual to see him smile or say something pleasant but, on the other hand, unpleasantness and aggression was an everyday thing. Over the weeks they'd had plenty of insights into his manner and, to some degree, had built up a resistance but not an immunity to him and his autocracy.

Leverett was the exception to the well-worn rule: his bite was worse than his bark!

Nevertheless, they couldn't take away from him the fact that he was a good teacher. He taught and they learned. He knew his business and, slowly, through him they endeavoured to know theirs.

With Cyril Jury, the gunnery and parade instructor, they learned because they wanted to please but with Geoff Leverett they learned through fear. Jury's way was the nicer and friendlier way but both methods of teaching achieved results. Although the boys feared and disliked Leverett, they learned from him and now, having attained first class status, they could look back with a certain amount of pride at their accomplishment. For the stage in their training syllabus and with the bulk of their early days uncertainties behind them, they had reached a high standard. They were good and what's more, they knew it.

TWO

Ginger didn't like Ganges. He wasn't quite as fanatical about getting discharged as some but he certainly didn't like the place. Nobody wanted to be there. Or that's how it appeared. If there was such a person who did like the place then they never made that fact known to the rest of them. Possibly there may have been a few – ex-Holbrook School inmates for example – who could tolerate conditions better, having already had a few years acclimatisation at Holbrook. But in the main, the goal of everyone was to get out of the place as quickly and painlessly as possible.

Although in some cases, not as painlessly. Some boys went to almost suicidal lengths to get out. In fact, past the point of 'almost' suicidal and actually went the whole hog. Sure enough, those poor boys, who really must have hated the place enough to make that ultimate decision, were, thankfully, few and far between. Nevertheless there were some, over the years.

Others, perhaps a little less determined, tried such stunts as pushing needles in their ears or whacking their knees with knotted wet towels.

Less ambitious still was those who continually went on the trot – running away, usually late at night – in the hope that eventually the authorities would get fed up with them and send them packing. That wasn't a very well thought out plan though because by definition, those escapades would have to be repeated several times with each recapture being rewarded with cuts.

Cuts was an upgraded version of schoolboy canning that the Navy retained exclusively for boys. The victim, once awarded cuts by the captain at Captain's defaulters, was escorted to an appropriate place, which was usually a room off the Quarterdeck, or sometimes more publicly in Nelson Hall, the drill hall bordering the parade ground, for the sentence to be carried out.

Word had it that persistent offenders had their punishment administered in public in Nelson Hall, although Ginger never witnessed any such humiliation. The buzz was that the miscreant was tied over a vaulting horse or maybe held down over a chair while the punishment was administered. The cuts varied from three, through six and up to twelve.

Ginger had never contemplated going on the trot. In his mind there was no point; they always came back, one way or another and, on top of that each 'returnee' would be subjected to those cuts – and they appeared to be rather painful.

A couple from 49 mess, a welsh lad imaginatively called Taffy, and a rather non-descript lad that hardly ever spoke to anyone, tried it on by slipping away one night but it was an attempt doomed to failure from the very start. They made no preparation; it was a spur of the moment thing. They had saved no money; they had secreted no bread away from the CMG (the dining hall) for their journey and they didn't know the way – even as far as Ipswich, or what their next move was if they somehow managed to reach that far.

Young 'non-descript' was from London, which was only about 50 or 60 miles away but still would have been quite an achievement for him to reach there. How Taffy ever hoped to reach those 'beloved valleys' that he never stopped talking about was a completely different tale and it was almost a dead cert he hadn't thought that one through.

Another thing they hadn't taken into consideration was what would they do if they did somehow manage to reach their homes. There would certainly have been a reception committee waiting to greet them and give them a free ride back!

On top of all those things against them, they also choose to do their moonlight flit in the depths of winter. Although there was no snow on the ground it was very cold and lonely out there at night in the dark, with nothing to eat at that time of year.

Ginger viewed going on the trot as a bit of an adventure but he could imagine just what his father would say if he turned up at home having run away. His father hadn't been very supportive when he had told them of his joining-up plans, with his 'you'll never pass the Navy's strict medical' and 'the Navy won't have any truck with sailors that can't swim', pronouncements, delivered with all the authority of someone who had never been anywhere or done anything.

The anticipated ridicule from his father announcing to everyone that his son had run away and the shame he would feel from the Biscuit family knowing, when their son Blondie was quite happy serving would have been too much for him. He would also have trouble facing Blondie, his erstwhile schoolmate, who had guided him to his first medical in London. He viewed it as an adventure alright and, if someone had asked him to abscond with them he most probably would have allowed himself to be talked into going. Luckily no-one asked and he was quite content to get his excitement second hand through other peoples adventures.

So he made up his mind to grit his teeth and stick it out, a bit like he did on that 'mast test' day when he was more afraid of the ridicule than the event itself. He hated the place but given the choice of staying put or running away, he decided to stay. He figured it was better to stay and be miserable than to suffer the ridicule and humiliation of being thought of as a deserter

16

by people back home. Anyway, people kept telling them that they had done the worst bit – they were first class now.

He had made a half-hearted attempt at *'working his ticket'* himself once, – which was what trying a crafty one on in order to gain their release was known as. The initial move he reasoned was to come up with something that would be difficult for the medics to disprove. A strained back was a good one but that had already been tried. A bad back was difficult to assess from a medical standpoint apparently but the pretence needed a lot of thought. It was something that had to be worked on every waking hour and not something that could be put to one side at 'stand-easy' or when a game of football was on offer.

The 'bad back brigade' blotted their copybook with inconsistency. They struggled and strained with rifle drill and gymnasium work in front of the instructors but would forget and leap out of bed to be first washed and dressed and waiting for the early morning cocoa. Or they would hurtle down the mess stairs in their eagerness not to be late before remembering to put on the 'can't hardly walk' routine when they realised that an instructor might have seen them. Those antics never lasted more than a couple of days before their light duties and excused doubling chitties were ceremoniously torn up before their eyes.

Another chap in 49 mess came up with continual bed wetting as a means of escape. He was convincing. He almost cracked it.

He would wake just before reveille, get a mug of water from the bathroom and tip it in his bed. Then, just as 'Charlie' sounded and the instructor came in, he would get 'caught' in the bathroom washing out his pyjama bottoms.

'Sorry sir,' he would put on his brave-little-boy apologetic act, 'I'm afraid I've wet the bed again.'

It went on for a while with him receiving sympathetic overtures from all quarters. The boys in the mess knew but didn't let on. The instructors allowed him special dispensation to hang his mattress cover in the airing room to dry during the day and the sick bay staff tried out various tests over a period of time to see if they could find the cause of his problem.

Eventually they turned him into the sick bay hospital as an in-patient, where he was woken every hour during the night and escorted for a pee. Only two nights of that and a miracle happened: his problem got better, never to return.

Ginger hadn't thought it through. Like most of them, he was blinkered and could only see ahead, at most, a few days at a time. Although he didn't like the place, he hadn't looked ahead to what he would do if he managed to get his discharge. Not many of them had thought that far ahead. Not to after their Ganges time was over and to where they would have a career of potentially twelve years of full time employment.

He hadn't even thought it out as far as him striding home to announce, loudly and proudly: 'I've managed to get my discharge.'

He hadn't thought how his announcement would be received. Almost certainly it would be with blank and partially confused stares, because they wouldn't understand and there could even be some sniggering from the *'I-told-you-sos'*.

He hadn't thought about what he would do next. No job; no money; no prospects; a failed naval career that was entirely of his own making – and not yet sixteen!

He hadn't realised it but he was just following suit. He was simply trying it on. It was a game of trying to beat the system. Although it wasn't treated as a game. The art of 'working your ticket' was a serious business. A serious business certainly but without that final piece of the jigsaw – what would they do if they were successful.

Ginger devised a scheme. He didn't tell anyone what he had in mind. It was a better plan that the old 'strained back' routine and a lot simpler. It didn't involve pretending to be in pain, only to forget at crucial moments.

He recalled his mother mentioning some years back about how he had weak ankles as a small boy. He figured that even if the powers-that-be checked, it would be documented somewhere in his medical history and that would give credence to his 'problem'. Hopefully that would leap frog him way ahead of the chancers, because he would have a genuine claim – even if he had just made it up!

There was nothing wrong with his ankles and he knew it. No-one else knew it; there was nothing to see so it couldn't be disproved.

So that was his plan when he approached Petty Officer Jury, the class instructor, one evening and said: 'I'd like permission to go to the sick bay, please sir.'

Boys were not allowed to just wander down to the sick bay whenever they felt the urge. First permission had to be obtained from the class instructor then, at the appointed time in the early evening, a sick parade was held on the quarterdeck. Anyone requesting to see a doctor would muster in a blue suit and carrying washing and shaving kit and a towel. They were marched down to face an interrogation from a sick berth staff member – to weed out the time wasters.

Ginger hadn't worried himself with the fine details. Too much detail could easily trip you up. His plan – as far as plan went – was to just present them with the basic case and let them work on the details. Too much detail from a patient could well look a bit suspicious.

It gave him a buzz knowing he was there with nothing wrong with him. He was in the process of beating them. It was a serious situation, nevertheless. If he was tumbled it would be jankers without a doubt for wasting the doctor's time and for skipping evening classes but, just the same he had to suppress a giggle when his feet were being examined.

His happiness was brought up with a jolt a few seconds later though when the doctor said, thoughtfully: 'I think we had better have you in.' Then he added, by way of reassurance: 'Don't worry. We'll soon have you as good as new. We know what the problem is.'

What the problem is! There is no problem! How can they find a problem when there isn't one? Ginger felt a wave of panic sweep over him. He briefly toyed with the idea of coming clean and admitting the whole thing was a fraud but luckily for him, his reasoning took over. That would only lead to even more trouble and he was in the middle of as much of that as he could handle at the moment.

This was getting out of hand. It had all started because – well, how had it started? He had tried out a scheme and it had worked. He hadn't thought ahead, even as far as what happens if it works. What had started out as showing a pair of fingers to the establishment had escalated and now he was lumbered. There was no choice; he had to play along.

'Right then, lad. Up to your mess, pack your pyjamas and deck slippers in your small case, tell your instructor what's happening and back here as quick as you can.' Those medics must have trotted out that line almost every day. It certainly appeared well used.

Ginger felt the bottom of his world falling away and dissipating into the darkness as he trudged back to his mess. Inside the mess passage, he ran into his old pal Mick Southern.

'I've really put my foot in it this time, Mick,' he said. 'The sick bay is going to turn me in.'

'Looks like you're on your way, old mate,' the tall Midlander replied with admiration.

'Not exactly what I had in mind,' Ginger mumbled gloomily. 'I think they're going to operate on my ankles. This isn't at all what I had in mind,' he continued, looking for consolation. 'I told them that my ankles sometimes give way when I'm marching or doubling. I don't know where I thought it would take me; maybe a spell of light duties or something but definitely not an operation in the hospital.'

19

'You've found the angle,' Mick told him, still full of admiration, 'maybe this will lead to your ticket.'

Mick's words hit him like a bolt of lightning; he was being supportive but what he said put things into perspective.

Ginger suddenly realised that he didn't want to get out. He had got himself caught up in playing the system without sparing a thought for the consequences. They were first class now; they were at least half way through their course; the worst was behind them. He still hated the place, the instructors and the routines but, at the same time he was feeling more comfortable with his situation. For the first time it had been brought into focus: he didn't want to leave.

He'd had lots of school friends at home. Everyone got along with each other and he had never felt isolated or alone in his village but this was different. With Mick's words came the dawning that he had never had so many friends. He was never alone. There were about fifty others in 49 mess. They were all one big family. Sure, families had their ups and downs and so did the inhabitants of 49 mess. Although the day-to-day routine was still on the harsh side, they were guided and protected every step of the way. They were fed, they were clothed, and they were paid. Fair enough, the pay wasn't much but seven and sixpence was better than five bob. He was secure. Not altogether happy but secure.

'Well, let's get my case packed and back down there,' he tried to sound cheerful, 'and hope they don't cut my legs off!'

They strolled as they talked until they reached Ginger's bed.

Ginger picked up his pyjamas and deck slippers and Mick, who had kept walking, reappeared with a magazine.

'This will help you pass the time,' he said, throwing the magazine into the open case. 'Take your writing kit as well. You'll have time to write a letter or two while you're down there.'

Mick had already had a short stay in the hospital for some minor ailment, so he was the experienced 'old hand'.

'I'll tell the petty officer what's happening, for you and don't worry, you'll be back here in no time,' Mick called after him.

'I bloody hope so,' mumbled Ginger to himself, as he headed down the mess stairs and out into the darkness.

From what few dealings Ginger had in the past with hospitals, he found they all smelled the same. It was a smell that you wouldn't necessarily remember but one that would come back to you just as soon as it was experienced again.

The ward he was assigned had that smell. It hit him the second he was escorted through the door.

He was ushered in through the door at one end of the long ward that stretched away into the distance, with beds along both walls and a dining table lengthways down the centre. A scene that was similar to every hospital ward throughout the country.

They were expecting him. There must have been some communication between the different departments while he was away collecting his pyjamas.

Inside the door his escort and he were met by a ward sick berth attendant. This chap was a small, fair-haired Scot. He seemed friendly enough from first impressions.

'So you're gonna visit us for a few days, eh?' he said.

Ginger didn't say anything. He didn't want to say too much until he had got his bearings. He was in pretty deep and he didn't want to say the wrong thing at this stage. It didn't look as if the medic expected an answer in any case. Ginger followed him to a bed about halfway down the ward on the right hand side.

'Here we are then,' Scottie said stopping at the foot of the bed, allowing Ginger to pass into the space alongside. 'Outa those clothes and inter your pyjamas then. I'll be back.'

As he began to get changed, Ginger had plenty of time to take in his surroundings. The occupant of the next bed was laying down with the blankets pulled up over his head so there was no way of telling who it was. A couple of people, he didn't know if they were boys or not, were sitting at the table. It looked like they were writing letters. Several more of the beds were occupied; some occupants were laying down, others were sitting up reading. No-one even acknowledged his presence.

This was all new territory to him. He had brought it all upon himself. It had got to the serious stage and it was too late to back out. The last time he was in hospital he was about seven years old and his mother was with him then. She did the talking and helped him settle in. This time he was on his own.

That Scottie, the ward orderly, told him to get undressed and into bed, so that was his next move. He pulled off his jumper and took his time folding it up. Trousers were next and they received the same attention, concertining the creases up in the prescribed manner. He was being very deliberate in an attempt to stop himself nervously looking around to see who, if anyone, was watching him. He felt vulnerable and self conscious, partly brought on by the unknown. He had got himself in deep. Now he was about to have an operation – and there was nothing wrong with him.

There were no lockers alongside the beds, only a silly little metal trolley on castors with a glass shelf on the top and another near the bottom. There was a little draw under the top shelf but that wasn't big enough to hold much. The suit and the rest of his clothes and boots were carefully placed on that bottom shelf. He figured that was where they were meant to go and also they were close enough for him to keep an eye on them, if they should change their mind and tell him to go.

After spending what seemed like an eternity, folding up his clothes and putting them on the shelf of the 'trolley', Ginger was at a loose end. He smoothed his pillow and patted his bedspread yet again but time seemed to pass very slowly.

After a while he felt that he could be attracting attention to himself – the very opposite of what he had been aiming for – by hanging around his bed and doing unnecessary things. So he walked over to the table and sat down on a vacant chair.

'Hello boys, how long have you been in here then?' he asked, addressing the two who had been sitting at the table ever since he came in.

As if upon some unheard command the two erstwhile letter writers finished their tasks, picked up their pads and pens and walked away to their respective beds. The older of the two, too old to be a boy, Ginger surmised, acknowledged him with a brief friendly nod, as he pushed his chair back before departing. Ginger felt uncomfortable and self-conscious. He was sorry he ever got started on this stupid prank.

Soon after, Scottie, the ward orderly returned.

'I told yee ter get inter bed,' he said.

Ginger looked round wondering why he had been singled out. The answer was obvious; he was the only one not in bed. The others knew the routine but none of them had bothered to put him in the picture.

'I was just on my way to the heads,' he lied.

'Well, move yersel' then,' Scottie replied. 'Yee should have thought of that earlier.'

Ginger scurried away. He didn't want to get singled out. That was never a good idea. Once you had their full attention you were a marked man. They never seemed to forget your face and that was the last thing Ginger wanted.

As he returned to the ward and headed for his bed, Scottie turned out the lights.

Although it was dark outside, there was still a small amount of light inside. It was too dark to read but light enough for him to see the 'shapes' in the occupied beds – and that Scottie was gone.

Ginger laid on his back staring at the ceiling as the thoughts of the last few hours replayed themselves over again. There's no last minute reprieve now, he thought. I'm right up the Swanee without that proverbial paddle. Events will have to take their course, come what may. It wasn't long before he was asleep.

In the morning he awoke to the sound of activity. Scottie came round with bowls of water and everyone was expected to wash and shave whilst sitting in bed.

Ginger wasn't a great shaver and could get away with it for a couple of days at a time and, he decided, this would be one of those days.

Suddenly he remembered he didn't have any soap. He had meant to get some that very evening but events had overtaken him and it had gone completely out of his mind. He sat there, faced with a bowl of water and no soap. He couldn't think of any way to cloud up that water. It sat there looking at him like a clear crystal stream. He rubbed his hands in it and splashed some on his face but when the ripples ceased it was as clear as it was when Scottie put it before him. He just had to brazen it out.

'Yee had a wash?' Scottie was back to collect the bowls.

'Oh yes,' Ginger lied.

'Did yee use soap?' Scottie asked suspiciously.

'Well of course I used soap,' was the innocent reply.

Scottie didn't look much older than the boys he was in charge of. He appeared hesitant about pursuing the matter any further.

'Well you must be a very clean boy then, that's all I can say,' he said.

Maybe with someone more senior, or older, to back him, he might have made a case of it. Instead he just took the bowl away and continued collecting the others without another word.

Ginger had got away with that one but he wondered how he would fare next time.

The next thing on the agenda was breakfast. Having been obliged to wash whilst sitting in bed, they were now expected to get up – those that could at least – and sit at the table.

Ginger was ready for breakfast. They were never over generous with food for the boys at Ganges. They were fed just enough to carry them through to the next meal. In the hustle and confusion of the night before, he had missed his supper. Now those early butterflies had turned into fighting bears, and were having a growling competition in his stomach.

The breakfast appeared on the table and bodies shuffled forward to take their place opposite a place setting. Ginger was a bit hesitant. He didn't know if they had certain places allocated. He was the new boy after all.

It was just as well he hung back.

'Not for you lad,' Scottie had reappeared just at the right moment. 'Did yee no read on yer bed?' he said, indicating his head toward Ginger's recently vacated bed.

Ginger followed the line of Scottie's gaze. Sometime during the night someone had hung a *'nil-by-mouth'* sign on his behead. He hadn't noticed it when he got up but it was there now all right. That was a bit of a blow; it meant no breakfast either.

'Yee're off te' theatre in a wee while,' Scottie informed him, in a matter of fact way. 'But yee'll be back in time for dinner, so don't worry.'

Don't worry. He had missed supper, he was about to miss breakfast and on top of that he was about to go to the operating theatre pretty soon. Why would he worry? What was there to worry about!

That breakfast smelled lovely. Ginger tried to stay away. He tried not to look at the breakfasts on the table. He tried not to look at anybody tucking in. He couldn't sit on his bed with that aroma nearby.

He ambled away and out through the ward door into the passage immediately on the other side. He was pointedly looking for something to take his mind off that breakfast. He briefly wandered into the toilet. He had found them the night before; it was familiar territory for him. Although familiar, he couldn't hang around very long for fear of arousing suspicion. Next to the toilets was another small room with a large sink. No-one was about, so he went in. They'd said nil-by-mouth but maybe a little sip or two of water wouldn't hurt. Those fighting bears were growling away something fearsome.

He couldn't see a cup or a glass and he didn't want to hang around too long looking for one, so he helped himself to a nice mouthful straight from the tap. That really felt good but he wisely didn't want to overdo it.

On the way out of the door, he ran into a medic. He hadn't seen this one before. He was a big, burly chap with black hair slicked back with oil.

'Why aren't you at breakfast?' he wanted to know.

'I'm nil-by-mouth, see,' Ginger told him, trying to sound more confident that he felt.

'Well get back to the ward then,' was 'Oily Head's' parting shot, as he opened another door and went in to what looked like an office.

Breakfast was finished as Ginger re-entered the ward. Ganges boys always ate at breakneck speed. People were already moving away from the table.

Scottie had been down at the far end of the ward and was on his way back. He met Ginger by the table.

'Come on then,' he said, 'help tee get these tables cleared and things picked up.'

He didn't stop as he spoke and he didn't look round as he passed on his way to the door.

You can get stuffed, mate, Ginger thought to himself. He had been allowed no breakfast, not even a cup of tea and he wasn't about to help them clean up.

Scottie had kept walking and had gone straight out of the door so Ginger continued on his way down to the bottom end of the ward where he found something interesting outside the window, until all signs of the meal had been removed.

Oily Head seemed to be the one that was running things now. There seemed to be a huddle round the table and he was one of them. Ginger hadn't noticed, until that moment, that the 'walking wounded' had managed somehow, to end up in the same place. Then, almost as quickly as they had come together, they drifted apart again.

Scottie was nowhere to be seen; he had gone. It appeared that Oily Head had issued orders. It looked like there was work to be done. No-one had called Ginger over to join them; he didn't know what was going on and he was in no hurry to find out. There were always front-runners whatever the situation. He had learned that in their early days in Hawke 49 mess. He figured to let the ones who wanted to be noticed do their thing while, at the same time, staying in the background looked to be the best solution for him. It had all the hallmarks of a work party but as he hadn't been asked to join in, he stayed out of their way. Volunteering wasn't part of his plans, it never had been.

He needn't have bothered himself however because Oily Head had him down for something completely different.

'I think we'll have you in bed now, young man,' he said. 'Visit the heads if you want to, then into bed. We've got to get you prepped.'

That last bit went right over Ginger's head. It was some kind of medical jargon and nothing he need bother himself about. He put his shoes on the shelf of his trolley-locker thing and obediently got into his bed.

Almost at once Oily Head returned. He was a big chap, more like a rugby player than a medical nurse. Although he was big he was not aggressive or intimidating as his size might lead one to infer.

Those first impressions Ginger had of him from their earlier encounter in the passage were wrong. Despite his size and appearing a bit on the cocky side, he was approachable.

'Someone will be along to see you in a while,' he told Ginger. Now that he had his attention Ginger thought he'd ask if the medic knew what was going to happen.

'I heard them talking,' he began. 'They were talking about manipulation, what's that mean then?'

'Oh, so that's what you're having done is it,' the medic replied. 'That's not too bad.'

'Yes but what is it?' persisted Ginger.

The medic, who had been standing at the foot of the bed, moved round to the side and leaned forward as if about to divulge some long kept secret. He stretched out his left hand, close to the bedspread and, at the same time, close to his body. His body was placed in such a way that shielded his hand from all prying eyes, except Ginger's. This was an intimate moment between the two of them. It looked as if he was about to share some personal confidence.

'See these fingers?' he began quietly. Without waiting for a reply, he continued. 'I hit a bloke so hard that I had to have manipulation on them to put them back in place.'

Ginger didn't know what to say. If Oily Head had punched someone hard enough to dislocate all his fingers, he didn't want to chance saying anything. He wasn't looking for a repeat performance. It crossed his mind that maybe Oily Head was coming an old salts tale to impress a youngster but he wasn't about to make those thoughts known – just in case.

'So you can see,' Oily Head continued in a much lighter vein, 'there's nothing to it. They'll put you out and wiggle your feet about a bit and you'll be back here, right as rain, in time for dinner.'

Ginger had another look at those fingers. They looked normal and there was nothing to see. Whether he had punched someone, as he had said, whether he had dislocated his fingers, whether he'd had manipulation on them, didn't matter any more.

A big weight had been lifted from his mind. It was as if someone had switched a light on in his head. Ginger was relieved. He felt like a different person; even the ward and the other patients seemed different. They were not going to cut his legs open. His operation simply involved wiggling his feet about a bit. As if by magic he was back to something like his old self.

By the time he had got over his mild euphoria, things were beginning to happen. Beds from the opposite side were being pushed across and in between those on Ginger's side until that entire side was clearer of everything.

The walking wounded were doing the work. Oily Head was the only staff member present and he was simply giving orders. After a sweep through, out came the polish and the 'bumper'.

The bumper was a large, heavy square block of wood on a long handle. The wood was covered by an old bit of serge. First it was used to push the polish about all over that side of the ward then, with a different bit of serge wrapped around, it was 'bumped' up and down by some luckless individual swinging the handle back and forth until the polished deck was deemed shiny enough.

After that the process was reversed. The beds were returned to their original positions and Ginger's side were pushed across and in between. Having been pushed over, Ginger had his back to proceedings but he guessed that an exact repeat performance was going on behind him. It occurred to him that he wasn't doing anything laying in bed and he could have been helping. Why they wanted him in bed so urgently, he had no idea but he was more than happy to lay there until the work was finished.

When he was back in his allocated slot and all cleaning materials had been stowed away, a doctor came to see him. After a few 'umms' and 'grunts' and with his eyes alternating between bits of paper he was carrying and looking at Ginger, the doctor made an attempt at bedside manner.

'Yes, that's fine,' he said with a false smile that appeared to be alien to him. 'We'll see you in a little while, old chap.'

With that he was gone. Apparently he had only come to see Ginger.

Not long after, Oily Head arrived with a syringe in a little dish. Ginger's face must have portrayed his feelings and the medic picked up on it.

'Oh, don't worry about this,' he said, realising Ginger was staring at that dish with it's sinister contents. 'It's only a tiny little prick, just to help your muscles relax.'

His tone was very calming and Ginger began to push up his sleeve.

Oily Head gave a little chuckle. 'Wrong end lad,' he said with a grin, at the same time indicating a little twirl with his finger. Ginger got the message and turned over.

Hardly had he undone his pyjama bottom when he received a resounding slap and, within a second or so, a slight metallic 'click' as Oily Head dropped the syringe back into its container. For a big man he certainly could be gentle. Ginger hadn't felt that needle at all.

'Right then lad, just lay there quietly and I'll be back in a while,' he said, picking up the dish and departing.

A raised voice brought Ginger out of his thoughts some time later. He hadn't been thinking of anything specific, he realised. He had been daydreaming. He had been almost asleep. He went to sit up to see what the noise was about but his head felt like it weighed a ton. He couldn't control it; he couldn't lift it off the pillow. He felt woozy. Everything felt unreal and that feeling persisted when they came for him. He seemed to remember lights above him and being wheeled along and people talking but he didn't know where he was – and what's more he didn't care.

He vaguely recalled someone who seemed a long way off, asking if he was comfortable and that he had tried to explain that his teeth had been removed by the dentist almost as soon as he arrived. But what he didn't know was that he had lost all interest in proceedings long before then.

When he came-to he found himself in a bed in that curtained-off bay-window area at the bottom of the ward. They had wheeled him there to recover in his own time. He had an awful thick head but this time he didn't try to sit up, he had already had that experience.

To add to his discomfort there was a very loud foghorn continually blasting away. It must have been foggy outside although he couldn't see out. There must have been a reason for that foghorn.

It seemed to be right under his window although it was probably on the other side of the river where the commercial river traffic was coming and going. Laying there, he willed that loud booming monster to stop and give his head a bit of peace but the answer was loud and clear – Noooooooo!

An hour or so later, as he regained full consciousness, his thoughts centred on his feet. Without lifting his head he pulled his legs up and stretched down to feel his ankles. They felt OK. There was no soreness or pain. He couldn't see if there was any bruising but they felt the same. He relaxed into his pillow. He had survived the ordeal. Although he'd had a few frightening moments, they were behind him now. No one had cottoned on to his 'fake' problem and he had wangled a day or two away from everyday routine.

Laying there in the semi-darkness, he couldn't help feeling a bit smug with himself. He had beaten the system and he had showed two fingers to the lot of them. He had played his best card and it had beaten theirs. All he'd needed then was to play his backing cards carefully and he was on his way home. Home. Home to what? He knew he didn't want to go. There was nothing there for him. It was his 'If-you-can-do-it-so-can-I' attitude in his make-up that had propelled him into the scheme in the first place. He just wanted to prove that it could be done. But it was a stupid prank and one that could have gone wrong in so many different ways. He had got it out of his system but it wasn't worth it. He hadn't thought it through. He wouldn't be trying any more schemes.

The next morning they discharged him back to full duties.

THREE

Ginger strode purposefully across the parade ground, eager to impress Petty Officer Jury. He had been discharged from the sick bay and was keen to join his class out there on the parade.

The class instructor spotted him heading their way and marched forward to meet him. Ginger couldn't help but marvel at the way Jury marched toward him. The man marched correctly; he stood to attention correctly; he saluted correctly and he dressed immaculately. Petty Officer Jury was Royal Navy through and through. Everything he did was perfection. They would have been hard pressed to find anyone better for a recruitment campaign.

'You got something wrong with your shoulder, lad?' he enquired in that slightly patronising way that he adopted when he addressed the boys.

Ginger's enthusiasm disappeared as quickly as a burst bubble. There was lots of things Jury could have greeted him with but that wasn't one of them. He had almost raced out of the sick bay complex as soon as they said he could go. He had hurried up to his mess to get changed into the obligatory rig-of-the-day before grabbing a rifle from the armoury at the end of Nelson Hall. He had seen his class out there involved in rifle drill and had taken it upon himself to draw a rifle, without waiting for Jury to tell him. He thought it might score him a point or two.

He had been in the hospital for a couple of days and now they had said he was fully fit again and ready to resume his duties. He naively thought Jury might have worried about him, seeing as he had been turned in and, maybe, was coming to tell him to take it easy for the remainder of the session.

The POGI's question caught him a bit on the wrong foot and the best he could manage was to stand there with his mouth open. 61 class were the only people on the parade ground and, as they were standing still, there was complete silence. Ginger had done his utmost to please and now he stood there feeling very small and vulnerable. There was no precise time logged when he left the hospital so he should have ambled around for a while. He could have stretched it out for at least another half an hour. He could have taken a lot more time getting changed in the mess and, with a bit of thought – and an element of luck – could have lasted out until dinnertime. He hadn't thought of any of that. His priority was to rejoin his class and, maybe, earn one of those tight little knowing smiles from Jury. But this he hadn't bargained for. The extra threads toward his green coat would have to be put on hold.

Jury didn't ask if he was all right to carry on with rifle drill. He didn't ask how he was after his spell in the hospital. He didn't even ask what had been wrong with him. All he wanted to know was if something was wrong with his shoulder.

Then the penny dropped. Despite being first class and knowing everything that they could teach him, he had marched smartly half way across Ganges parade ground with his rifle on the wrong shoulder!

Petty Officer Jury had a patronising, almost sarcastic, manner about him and his short, sharp 'naval messages' type of speech always cut straight to the heart. In all fairness to the man, he was not intimidating or threatening like Leverett, the other class instructor or Batchelor, the assistant divisional officer. Those two were confirmed nasties and they were willing to demonstrate that fact without any provocation whatsoever.

Jury wasn't over friendly and his quiet manner could never be taken for granted. In all probability all new class instructors were told not to form any friendships with the recruits and to keep things strictly on a 'them-and-us' basis. Many, if not most, interpreted that into an invitation to turn into little Hitlers for the duration of their time as Ganges class instructors.

PO Jury wasn't nasty. He didn't follow the lead. He was his own man. Nevertheless his short, sharp, straight to the point 'naval messages' utterances were as sharp as a razor and hit the bulls eye every time. As time had progressed the boys found they could let the screaming and shouting wash over them, without any of it sinking in – but with Jury it was a different story. He didn't waste breath or energy on belching out unnecessary venom but his quiet 'verbal arrows' never left the recipient in any doubt. They hit home to the very core every time.

Petty Officer Cyril Jury was a very good instructor. He wore fore and aft rig of an established petty officer with his GI's badge on one arm and three good conduct badges on the other. He knew his job and was able to teach in an easy to understand matter of fact way. The inmates of Hawke 49 mess learned from him and learned well. Where some instructors method of teaching was through intimidation and fear and learning particular segments parrot fashion, until their charges could repeat it word perfect but maybe not understanding, Cyril Jury appeared to want to teach.

Whether on the parade ground or in the classroom, he would go over even a minor point time and time again if someone failed to grasp it.

Elevations, tangents, trajectories, aircraft recognition, were like a foreign language in the classroom for the first couple of times but with POGI Jury's patient teaching, after a while they became as familiar as the chap in the next bed in the mess. Even on the parade ground, forming squad, changing direction on the march and counter marching, all became second nature.

Chief Bumble had taught them the basic marching drill in the Annexe and they thought they were pretty hot stuff by the time they got to the main establishment. But apart from having learned which foot to step off with and how to swing the opposite arm and how to stand to attention and at ease properly, they quickly realised they were complete novices. Particularly when rifles were introduced.

Once again Ginger had landed on his feet. The army cadet training he'd had prior to joining up came in handy once more. It had held him in good stead during the Annexe days where he almost had a holiday while the rest of his class struggled to reach the level he had joined up with. Then, over into the main establishment and into training proper he had a head start with rifle drill, thanks to that army cadet training that he had paid very little attention to.

As always, the Navy way was slightly different but, for once, their way was easier. The army wanted straight fingers whenever possible but the Navy liked to see rifles grabbed hold of firmly. Their method was simpler and it saved a lot of weapons being dropped.

Jury had taught them well. He had brought them on gradually until they had reached an acceptable standard. On the parade ground they felt that they could hold their own against all comers. They had been told that there was still room for improvement and, although they felt confident, if there was a higher level to be achieved they were ready and willing, with Jury at the helm. They liked Jury and, without exception, they were eager to strive for that little bit more. If he thought it was possible then it was possible.

They had to concede, if somewhat grudgingly, that Leverett, their other class instructor, was also a good teacher. Or, at least, he knew his business and they learned from him. His method was far more aggressive and he had that 'I-must-be-obeyed-immediately' attitude about him. He was their seamanship instructor and he knew his job.

Although he taught seamanship Leverett was also a gunnery rate. He had a first class QR1 badge on one arm and his petty officer's crossed anchors and one good conduct badge on the other. Whereas PO Jury wore the fore and aft rig of an established petty officer, Leverett was an *acting* petty officer and still wore square rig, the same as the boys.

The two instructors dressed differently; they acted differently; their teaching methods were different and they looked different. Jury was the smaller of the two in height but had a little more bulk on him. He had a non-committal face that rarely betrayed his thoughts. Leverett appeared to be taller than he was because he was thin. He always wore his hat pulled right down to his ears with little tufts of ginger hair protruding from under. He had a red face probably brought about because he always shouted at full volume. The inflated veins on his neck were most likely as a result of pressure on them from all that shouting.

Jury would go over and over things as many times as he thought necessary until he was sure that every one of his charges understood but Leverett usually only wanted to explain things once. His approach was a predictable: 'Stop cackling your fat and pay attention.'

In the seamanship classroom he would impart the information until *he* felt everyone should have grasped it, then he would ask if there were any questions. Naturally there were none because they were all reluctant to get singled out for his full attention. Sometimes however, met with a sea of blank faces, he would come up with a question himself and woe betide anyone unfortunate enough to catch his eye, if they didn't know the answer.

The inmates of 49 mess may have learned their seamanship through fear and intimidation, but learn it, they certainly did. Ropes and splices; knots and hitches; rule of the road and navigation; lights by night, sounds by day; lights on ships, lights on buoys; dropping anchor, weighing anchor; lowering and raising the seaboat; steering by compass, steering by magnetic tape; were all learned to a very high standard, through the fear of failure and incurring Leverett's displeasure.

Ganges was a teaching establishment. That was the sole reason for its existence. It was geared up entirely for the teaching of young boys. Other than the class instructors who, in the main, stayed with their class from beginning to end, there were also 'occasional teachers'. People who played a significant part in the development of the boys' education but on an ad-hoc basis.Such people as PTIs.

There were those who were attached to each division and taught physical training to their divisional members and there were others who coached specialised subjects, such as water polo and diving, or those that took the continual stream of backward swimmers who descended upon them from the Annexe every six weeks. Others were involved in field sports like football, cricket, rugby, hockey, etc. and the track events down on the lower playing field.

Other part time instructions that were available, included the bugle band, a camera club, a music club and, although Ginger kept well away, a dancing class. Even the parsons played a part for any of the boys, or ships company for that matter, who were that way inclined.

But the bane of their young lives were the schoolies. These were schoolteachers specifically employed by the Navy – and given officer rank to instruct boys in schoolwork subjects. Ginger reflected the first time school, and more to the point school classrooms, was sprung upon them, that they had left school behind and had joined the Navy. They had become men almost ready to join the Fleet and then the Navy had thrown them back into school again.

The school rooms were not much different from those they had forsaken only a short year earlier and now they were back in amongst it again. This time interspersed with the usual maths, English and geography were new subjects like navigation: how to plot a course and dead reckoning; mess bills and stores ordering; mechanics (nothing to do with mending car engines!); mapping out the force fields of bar and horseshoe magnets, and Magnetism and Electricity!

'Mag and Elec' as it was known was confusing to say the least. It was taught in an obscure dialect of Arabic or something similar and not one of them understood what it was all about. None of them could figure out what earthly use Mag and Elec would be to them in the furtherance of their career. Particularly Ohm's Law. Ohm's Law was drilled into them every time they had a school session:

> *'Ohm's Law states that the ratio between the ends of a conductor and the current passing through it is a constant. Ohm's Law only applies if the temperature is a constant.'*

They all had to learn it and repeat it singsong fashion, all together. That wasn't too bad because, they all had an approximation of the words although not necessarily in the correct order and saying it together helped each other along. Luckily they were never asked to explain what it meant.

For some unknown reason Ray Leeward was singled out to stand in front of the class and repeat the dreaded Ohm's Law. How he came to be singled out was never asked. The rest of the class were just glad it wasn't them.

Poor old Ray stuttered and stammered but had no more idea than any of the rest of them. Lady Luck must have been having a good day that day and she took him under her wing as the bell to end their session rang out and they hurried to get out of there.

But not before the schoolie had declared a trip over the mast for everyone if Ray couldn't recite it, word perfect, at the next session.

The following morning, after a great deal of swotting during the night and a few words of encouragement from the tough guys who didn't fancy that mast excursion, Ray played a blinder and everyone breathed a sigh of relief. Even the schoolie two-ringer smiled that smile that says, 'At last I've taught them something'.

Ray Leeward saved their bacon that morning. He became the guru of Mag and Elec. He repeated the required text perfectly – although he had no more idea of what it meant than any of the others!

If Magnetism and Electricity had taught them anything, what was it and would it ever prove to be of any use to them as their time progressed. There didn't appear to be a situation where knowing the route of the force fields of a magnet would help them in any way whatsoever. Or how that situation might ever arise. As for electricity, they had electricians to handle anything in that line and boy seamen – first class or not – would never be allowed near anything so potentially dangerous.

Why they had been introduced to the subject in the first place was a mystery. Most of them hadn't grasped it and those few that had, wondered what they had actually learned. The only explanation they could come up with was that so many sessions were allocated to schoolwork and those sessions had to be filled somehow.

One particular schoolie, who was a bit more lenient than most, would keep them entertained by showing old MOD instructional films. Films on how to load and fire various ships guns or how to load and fire torpedoes or how to tackle fires. Then he would make them more interesting by running the action sequences backwards. Maybe they didn't learn a lot about firing ships armament or fighting fires but at least they passed an enjoyable session or two and had a good laugh – a rare commodity at Ganges.

Another chap Ginger cottoned onto had been tasked to teach them woodwork. The woodwork school, or shed as it turned out to be, was across the main road and down past the Annexe gate and right down to the very bottom of the Annexe road where there was a collection dilapidated old huts.

There didn't appear to be a woodworking course in the strict sense of the word and the new man either couldn't teach or didn't want to. He seemed as pleased as the boys in his charge to be out of sight and out of the way.

It didn't seem that woodwork was part of the school curriculum because the venue was quite small and there was no full time instructor. The place didn't look as if it was in constant use. They didn't know why they were there. Woodwork had been sprung on them one morning at the school gates and they had been marched straight over.

At their first session, as soon as they realised they would be left to their own devices, the front-runners, the ones who always wanted to get noticed, made a beeline for the wood turning lathe to show off their skills and maybe score a few points with 'Sir'.

Ginger didn't know what to do. There was plenty of tools and bench spaces but no inspiration. He had never been much of a carpenter. At his school back home they had a full day every second week in the carpentry shop but he had struggled. Now he figured he had better look busy, if not to say businesslike. He found a small bit of wood and spent some time squaring a pencil line across it, then he sawed the end off along the line. Removing his handiwork from the vice he held it up and studied it thoughtfully, one way and then another, eyeing along his recently sawn line. He continued studying his piece of wood thoroughly until he was certain the schoolie instructor wasn't paying him any attention before consigning his masterpiece back to the bin.

In the waste bin he noticed a discarded block shaped into a yacht hull. Someone had taken a great deal of time and trouble shaping and sanding it before, apparently, being forced to leave it behind. That was his salvation. That yacht hull became a permanent fixture under his arm as he wandered about. Sometimes it was held up and measured carefully or, occasionally it was placed in a vice and studied from all angles, before returning to its permanent mooring under his arm.

There were small lockers where half completed work was kept until the next visit and Ginger made a point of stowing his pride and joy away, very carefully, making sure it was labelled clearly so everyone would know it was his.

Their woodworking classes seemed to have been a mistake and were cancelled after only a few sessions. Whether they had been assigned there in error, or whether they had caught up with the regular schoolwork and no-one could come up with anything else for them to do, or maybe it was a reward for 'doing so well' with that Mag and Elec episode, who could tell.

Anyway, whatever the reason, the schoolie announced during what was to be their last time in the place, 'No more boats to be made.'

Ginger felt a tinge of sadness as he returned his racing yacht hull – or was it the beginnings of a schooner or a galleon – back to the waste bin. It had become a good friend to him. It looked exactly the same as it did that first time. During those woodworking sessions it had not even acquired as much as an additional pencil mark!

Although they were obliged to spend substantial amounts of time in the school block preparing for their academic qualification of ET1, which would be taken later after they had left Ganges, schoolies, by and large were the 'out of sight, out of mind' kind of worry. There were one or two that were a bit full of themselves, exercising their new found power and authority but their reign was short lived and restricted to an hour or two, at most.

Their regular man was a borderline case. In a relaxed moment, early in their acquaintance, he had told them he had been a Royal Marine sergeant before reincarnating himself as a Navy schoolteacher. He had a touch of megalomania about him and he had his moments but, at the same time, compared to Leverett and Batchelor, he was a pussy-cat. In one of their more informal moments, he had enlightened them with the tongue-in-cheek gem: 'Royal Marine sergeants are equivalent to Navy lieutenants anyway!'

It was him that had threatened the mast excursion, over the Ohm's Law incident.

Although that rotten Mag and Elec business took up a lot of their time, he also taught them basic navigation. There were piles of old charts in a cupboard and he would hand them out. The same chart for everyone. He would then give them certain co-ordinates as their starting point, followed by a course and course corrections, including wind and current variations. Alternatively, he would sing out certain bearings from prominent features on shore and have them work out a dead-reckoning position.

All went well with navigation under his teachings and he visibly stiffened with pride when they all scored exceedingly high pass percentages.

Those charts were used over and over again by each successive class and although the pencil lines were rubbed off, little did he realise that enough of it remained for them to just retrace the previous plotters work. By giving the same course and bearings each time, the final positions had to be the same. 61 class soon cottoned on to that fact and from then on, navigation was a doddle.

It was during one particular school session that talk of religious instruction came up. This, in turn, led to the question of anyone wishing to attend confirmation classes in the padres office. As these classes would be undertaken instead of school room sessions, Ginger was quick to respond.

He knew that it was something his mother would like him to do and that it could help him score a few points at home. He had the basic grounding anyway, from his time spent as a choirboy before he joined up, plus there was talk of a certificate at the end.

So, partly to please his mother but mostly to get away from that interminable schoolwork for a while, he enrolled.

He had seen the parson, from afar at the compulsory Sunday service in the Church of Scotland chapel, each Sunday morning but had never actually spoken to him. Some of the boys stayed behind after the service for the usual meet-the-padre sessions, where sometimes girls from the local church would also be there but Ginger had other ideas. As soon as that last 'amen' had sounded, he was out of there. After all, by then it was almost dinnertime.

He rather assumed that the parson would be different and friendlier than other Ganges officers, maybe a bit like the local vicar back home. He visualised the padre's office to be like a vicarage, with easy chairs and, maybe, a settee. Even, perhaps, a cup of tea sometime during their friendly chat.

Their first meeting put him straight on a few things. For a start he was shorter than he appeared to be on Sundays, at a distance and dressed in all his finery. The vicarage had transformed itself into a drab little brick built office at the south end of the quarterdeck. There were six of them knocking on the door that first time.

'Come in. Enter,' was the response to their knock.

They entered and stood facing the parson, who was sitting behind a desk.

'Right then. First things first. I'd better have your names.'

They all tried to talk at once.

'Stop. Take a seat on those chairs behind you. I thought there would have been more of you than this.'

They shuffled back self-consciously and sat on the straight-backed wooden chairs. There were no easy chairs or settee.

'That's better. Now I'll have your names one at a time. On second thoughts, I'll read them off the front of your shirts.'

With that, they stepped forward, one at a time and stood in front of the desk while the he copied down names that were stamped above their breast pocket.

Ginger's illusions of the friendly village parson were shattered. That man was acting just like a typical Ganges officer; in one sense, worse that a Ganges officer. No one in the entire establishment had ever demanded to read their name from their shirt before. He felt let down, betrayed even. It was as if they didn't have a mind of their own, as if they were not capable of remembering their own names. That kind of treatment made them feel like criminals.

Not a good introduction to God's company. Talk about fellowship of goodwill.

The whole confirmation episode only lasted about six sessions, over as many weeks and, after learning that there was no such thing as an easy ride at Ganges, parson or no parson, the time passed in an uneventful blur. It all came good on Sunday March 28, 1954 when Ginger got his certificate and sent it home to his mum.

Those confirmation classes broke the monotony of the schoolwork. But after the confirmation itself had taken place there were no more sin bosun sessions although the schoolwork continued. That short interlude of religious instruction came as a welcome relief as it got them out of the school for a while. The sessions were comparatively easy because their parson was the preacher type. He was the sort of person that liked to preach. As long as he had an audience he would rabbit on. He rarely asked questions. All they had to do was sit still and look interested, which suited Ginger a treat because all he was interested in was getting out of that school as often as possible and picking up his certificate. This did the trick on both counts.

There was not much to chose between the schoolies and PTIs. Both had a job to do and both were the out-of-sight, out-of-mind type of instructor. That didn't mean that they were a pushover. In most walks of life there is usually someone who is a soft touch and it was true of those departments but those people were always balanced out by the aggressive sort, who have an axe to grind. Both the school and the gymnasium were hard work in their own way but their sessions were preferable to being with Leverett or Batchelor.

Sessions for both places, the school or the gym, their instructor would leave them at the door and that would be the last seen of them until the end of the period. As time progressed the instructors didn't even accompany them that far and they would be left to make their own way under the supervision of Daisy their badge boy.

Before arriving at Ganges, Ginger had never done any gymnasium work. There was no gym at his school. Sure, they had played football and cricket and had ridden their bikes for miles, so they were probably as fit as the average schoolboy although he lacked the technical language and the names for the various bits of the apparatus. Inside the gymnasium was like being on the surface of the moon to him for his first couple of sessions in the place.

It was interesting work and probably the next best thing to sports. For their first few weeks all they did, mainly, was stamina building exercises, running round and round with an occasional sprint from one end of the gym to the other. Their divisional PTI was a small chap who quickly acquired the name of Mighty Mouse. He was a reasonable man and they built up their stamina and speed without realising it. He tried to make the sessions under his command as interesting as possible and they learned. They learned faster than was expected of them and they were happy doing so. There was no fear or intimidation; 61 class enjoyed their gymnasium time. It was a pity that they couldn't say the same for periods under Leverett or Batchelor.

In addition to their course work standard, there was the extra burden of training for the Festival of Remembrance. For the third year on the trot, Ganges was to provide the maze marching display for the festival at the Albert Hall, in London. Normal PT sessions were put on hold as 'festival fever' took precedence. All three gymnasia were commandeered as boys were put through their paces at breakneck speed with PTIs watching every movement, looking to weed out any one that they considered to be not up to standard.

All three gyms were attached to each other and decreased in size as their number increased. Number one gym was the main gym and the biggest. The likely candidates for the display training went on in there with those weeded out being dispatched to number two gym next door. Number two gym was a replica of number one, where exactly the same routines were being carried out. It was a pool from which candidates for the main squad could be interchanged with those that had a momentary lapse of concentration. There was a steady stream of boys passing to and from one squad to the other. Maybe it was a pre-arranged plan to keep everyone's mind focused. Not that they needed any incentive. A trip to the Albert Hall in London was incentive enough.

Nevertheless, the training was excessive. The complicated routines had to be learned and gone over again and again until everyone was absolutely certain of his part in the overall picture. But the patronising way they had of singling out boys that they thought were not up to standard, was ridiculous. PT staff were stationed all round the outside edge of the squad and the senior trainer out in front.

'Sit down' …. 'Stand up'…. 'Sit down' …. 'Stand up'…. and so it went on in rapid succession. There was absolutely no reason for it, other than to whittle the numbers down. Anyone that was a bit behind with getting down or getting up would be dispatched to number two gym through the connecting door.

Ganges boys were fit; there was no question about that. The mere fact that they were at Ganges meant that they were fit, there was no way they could have been otherwise. They double-marched everywhere they went, all day long; they spent every afternoon playing sports; they spent many periods on the river in boats with big, heavy oars; they swam and they spent lots of time in the gymnasium. They were training to perform a display at the Albert Hall; two displays if you count the afternoon dress rehearsal. Apart from having to learn the maze marching routine, which wouldn't have taken long, they could have taken it in their stride. If the authorities had invited cadets, scouts, reservists or territorials for that matter, to perform the display, it would have been a different story. Those people were part-timers and fitness and training would have been an issue but Ganges boys trained all the time. They were untouchable.

So all that 'jump up, sit down, roll over' rubbish was just a patronising way to pick what they considered the best people for the job. All that was required was for them to chose a senior class and train them up. Any class in the place could have done it. The repetitious rubbish served no useful purpose and even the most dedicated began to lose interest.

Ginger enjoyed the gymnasium work. He wasn't that good but over the weeks had become efficient to say the least. He wanted to perform in front of all those crowds at the Festival of Remembrance but all this unnecessary carry-on knocked the edge off his enthusiasm and he no longer wanted to be part of it.

When the next 'stand up, sit down' routine reared its head yet again, Ginger deliberately got up a fraction later than everyone else, he knew what he was doing and he was not disappointed. Three muscle bound arms, with outstretched fingers pointed at him and then indicated the door to number two gym. From then on it was simply a case of being deliberately slow in there until he received the sad news that he was no longer required for the display team, or the reserves.

Daisy and a couple more from 49 mess made the team and the trip.

FOUR

The heavy gun battery was way down almost on the foreshore and behind the signal tower, which stood tall with its barrel shaped body and conical roof.

They enjoyed going to the gun battery. It was fun. It was still hard work and they were there to learn but being around a real life-sized twin four-inch mounting brought things into perspective somewhat.

They had spent time letting go and weighing anchor in the seamanship block, and they had a taste of the wheel on a contraption that chugged round, but they were models and this gun was real. It looked real, it felt real, it was real. If they had live ammunition it would have fired for real - not that the people of Felixstowe, Harwich and Parkstone on the other side of the rivers Orwell and Stour would have appreciated it.

To all intents and purposes the twin four-inch was real. The only difference between their mounting and those on a ship, was that the ones aboard ship fired live ammunition and they had to content themselves with firing a shell made of wood with brass trimmings. But despite that minor shortcoming, it was a real gun and not a model and it helped to make them forget Ganges for an hour or so every once in a while.

Most of their first session was taken up by PO Jury showing them round and explaining the names of the various parts and their functions.

The boys of 61 class marvelled at every part of that gun as they listened to the POGI's explanations. Everything from the tip of the muzzle to the workings of the breech mechanism, to the fuse setting machine and fuse clock to the trainer and layer position and jobs. Undoubtedly many of them were thinking that they would be manning one of those positions for real in the not too distant future when they had left Ganges for good and had joined a ship at sea.

Jury took them through every operation from the placing and removing tampions – an expanding screw cap that fitted into the end of the barrels when the guns were not in use – to testing circuits with a sawn-off end of a brass shell and a real, but small, charge.

They also learned how the fuse machine grabbed the fuse end of the shell and twisted on a fuse setting and the function of the fuse operator. How the trainer and layer followed pointers in dials set in front of them, to turn the mounting and raise and lower the barrels. Pointers similar to those of the fuse setter, who also doubled as communications, followed to ensure each shell had the correct setting before being placed in the breech by the loaders. He showed them how the breech operator worked the breech mechanism lever and an electrical switch, called the interceptor, which completed the electrical circuit and allowed the gun to fire.

They loved it. They jumped on it and clambered all over it. It was solid and there was nothing to break. It smelled like a real ships gun.

After their familiarisation Jury got them started on the job in hand. They had been told how each segment worked in conjunction with other segments to make the whole thing work. Then it was their turn to become part of that operation.

There were eight positions on each gun and sixteen eager beavers needed no second invitation to leap into those positions. It was like being allowed to play with a giant Mecanno set – but potentially more dangerous.

PO Jury was not a gung-ho merchant and as soon as the boys were in position he made it quite clear that they were not to touch anything or do anything unless he said so.

'I've been around ships armament for a long time,' he told them, 'and accidents happen. Mostly they're caused by people not listening or following orders. We don't want any accidents to trainees in my charge.'

Until a proficient standard was achieved, all manoeuvres at Ganges were carried out by numbers. In their early days in the Annexe, even turning right or left while standing still, was carried out one stage at a time, by numbers.

Gun drill was no exception. For their first couple of sessions no-one did anything unless Jury said so. All their basic sessions were taken up by running through a routine from start to finish and then again with everyone changing places until all of them had a turn in each position.

He would shout orders and they had to pretend not to hear him until they had been repeated by the communications number, who was seated at his fuse machine.

'Just like on a ship,' Jury told them. 'No-one hears anything until the communications number repeats the order relayed through his earphones.'

After removing the tampions and checking circuits, the fun began. The three loaders on each gun grabbed a dummy shell and the first one was placed on the fuse machine. It was pushed forward on rollers until the fuse operator turned a handle that set the correct fuse on the shell nosecone. Then the shell was shoved into the breech where the breech-block would slam shut.

This was followed by a series of shouts.

'Trainer on!' from the trainer in the left hand chair at the front.

'Layer on!' from the gunlayer on the other side in the right hand seat.

'Interceptor closed,' from the breech operator.

Then PO Jury would go into his routine.

'Shoot.'

'Fire.'

'Bang.'

'Gun recoil.'

'Gun run out.'

Why he felt it necessary to run through that entire sequence every time a round fired was anybody's guess. Maybe he thought it lent atmosphere.

The breech operators then opened the breech, allowing the loaders to catch the wooden shell as it was ejected.

So it continued .... loader, fuse setter, fuse operator, trainer, layer, breech operator, over and over again, with Cyril Jury adding his contribution as each sequence progressed. The only let-up was a periodic rotation of positions until everyone, including spare numbers, had worked a full sequence in every position.

As per usual, the front-runners wanted to be noticed and have, what they considered, the important positions. While they were jostling each other to be first to catch Jury's attention Ginger would slip quietly into the fuse setters seat on the left gun. The right gun setter had the communications and all the shouting to deal with as well as the fuse dials to follow. All Ginger had to do on the left gun position was to follow the pointers on his dial and keep a low profile. He was sitting down while most of the others were racing about trying to impress. The first run of the session was usually the longest. By the time all the pre-firing checks had been completed and someone had been put straight on some minor point of procedure, he had usually been sitting down unnoticed for something like half an hour before a position rotation was called for.

Gun drill in the gun battery could be hard work but it was interesting and entertaining. There were stories of boys having to hold shells above their head or even carrying one up and down Faith, Hope and Charity, the stone steps that led past the battery, but Jury wanted none of that. With the front runners like Dereham, Doug Raines and Sweaty Gillette doing the bulk of the work, they were content. They were happy and with them being happy, POGI Jury was happy. They were doing something that they enjoyed. Everyone was happy. Life was sweet.

PO Jury drummed into them at their first session how dangerous big guns could be and every once in a while he would repeat those warnings. He had made the situation quite clear before they ever went near the mounting and, throughout their time in the heavy gun battery, he was ever vigilant. Occasionally he would stop a drill mid-flow when he spotted something or someone out of place.

'That's how accidents happen!' he would bellow.

Despite his continual warnings, complacency brought on by familiarity did creep in and a few near accidents tended to show how easily – and quickly – a smooth run could turn into a disaster.

A touch of complacency coupled with 'I'm-an-old-hand-now-and-I-could-do-this-with-my-eyes-shut' attitude was Gingers downfall at one drill and could easily have spelt big-time disaster.

They had been in and out of the battery many times over the weeks and although some of the novelty had worn off the sessions were still enjoyable. By this time every one of them could man and operate every position on the mounting and their drill times were getting faster and faster.

They had 'closing up', 'clearing away', 'testing circuits' and 'ready for action' down to a fine art whomever was in whatever position. PO Jury had brought them on slowly until they had achieved a very high standard. As with the parade ground he wanted to teach and, with him as their tutor, they wanted to learn

On this particular drill, Ginger was breech mechanism operator on the right gun, which meant that he had to operate the breech mechanism lever with his left hand. That lever was quite heavy and, under certain conditions, it was aided by a very strong spring. Although working left handed was tricky it was not too bad but, like most other positions, concentration was required at all times.

Concentration was never Ginger's strong suit and as the end of the session approached on that particular day his mind was elsewhere. The last run through had been called and completed and the last wooden shell fired and ejected. This left the breech open and tension on that very strong spring.

PO Jury called for the breeches to be closed and the mounting secured.

All that was required from Ginger, apart from his full attention, was to take the weight of that lever and lower it slowly. But, with his mind on the imminent dinner only a few minutes away, he just released the holding catch, forgetting that the lever was under full tension from that spring. The lever, released from pressure, dropped with an almighty crash like a ton weight. As it did so, the protruding handle just brushed his top lip, no more than the light touch of a pencil, but enough to frighten the living daylights out of him. Half an inch closer and it would have taken the bottom half of his face away.

Jury was there instantly. He looked worse than Ginger.

'You all right lad?' his face was full of concern. 'Where did it get you? Get him down from there.' He really was a nice man. His concern was genuine.

A few nearby stepped forward to help. Ginger realised what a narrow escape he'd had and his face must have gone a funny shade of white but he was perfectly all right.

'I'm OK,' he began. He could hardly believe it was his voice that said that. The others who had all gathered round, including PO Jury, must have noticed that nervous quaver. 'It never touched me.'

A look at the faces staring up at him told him that he hadn't convinced anyone.

'No, really, I'm pretty lucky, It never touched me,' his voice sounded more like his own again. His momentary scare had passed now although a few close by and particularly Jury, looked to be in some kind of temporary shock.

'Let's have a look at you,' said Jury, reaching up to help him down from the platform that was not much more than a foot off the deck. 'Sit on the edge of the platform and let's have a look at you.'

'Really, it never touched me. It was close but it just missed me,' Ginger tried to convince Jury who was busy looking inside his upper lip.

A thought suddenly struck him. They were old hands now and in the confusion he almost forgot the golden rule: *A green coat should be worn at all times and, in any kind of situation, clearing ones own yardarm first is an absolute priority.*

'Er, I'm afraid my hand slipped off the lever handle, sir. It must have been because we were getting a bit sweaty.'

He wasn't about to admit that he had forgotten the lever was under tension or that his mind was elsewhere.

The last few minutes of the period flew by as the breeches were closed and the mounting secured, while he sat recuperating, as per PO Jury's orders.

Ten minutes later, when they were in the Central Mess Galley for dinner, Ginger got to thinking about his near miss and how close to disaster he had been. That lever had dropped with enough force to have knocked his upper teeth out and carried away his entire jawbone. It was certainly his lucky day with the God of Fortune smiling kindly toward him.

It was a pity that those gods were not smiling as favourably a few months earlier when the dentist had done what that breech mechanism lever had almost done.

He had only joined up a week or so previously when they were all marched over from the Annexe to the dentist in the main establishment. All new recruits were obliged to have a dental check-up as part of their joining routine. Ironically the Dental Block was almost next door to the heavy gun battery.

They were marched over one afternoon and most of them sailed in one door and out the other with little or no work to be done. There were a few booked in for an odd filling and such but nothing major – except Ginger. The moment he sat in the chair the dentist took an instant dislike to his teeth. The front two were slightly crossed and had started to show signs of decay at the crossover point.

After a lot of tut-tut-tutting and mumbling technical jargon to the SBA clerk who was taking notes, the dentist made another appointment for a few days later when a full set of impressions were made.

A couple of weeks later they had a lecture from a chap who had come over to the Annexe. The entire recruitment were mustered in the NAAFI canteen room on the left hand end of the Dining Hall to hear that chap drone on about the correct way to clean teeth. Ginger was chuffed to notice that the set of teeth being used for demonstration purposes were his. He could tell by the crossed over two in the front.

After that no mention was made of teeth or dentists until about a month later when he had moved over the road and into Hawke Division, when, one morning, out of the blue, he was told he had been summoned to the dentists for treatment. Just before leaving the mess he had a final check in the mirror and made a mental note to suggest to the dentist what teeth needed to be removed and which could be adjusted and saved.

But when he got to the chair the dentist wasn't interested in anything he had to say and, after more jargon mumbling to the SBA assistant, pulled out five right across the front and drilled and filled the majority of the remainder. A pre made set were then forced into the holes where the others had been removed, with torrents of blood running everywhere. Ginger didn't get to have a say or offer an opinion.

The incident with the gun lever brought it all back to him as he sat eating his dinner because that dental saga finished just at dinnertime and he had been forced to eat his dinner and several subsequent meals with a very tender mouth and with blood everywhere.

After his new teeth had been inserted Ginger was told to wait in an adjoining room. It was a bare room with just two wooden chairs and an old china sink in the corner. He made several trips to the sink to try to spit out blood that was still running freely. Spitting was not an easy thing to do with a numb mouth but he persevered. It was better than sitting still.

A different SBA came in after a while with a kettle to fill at the sink, presumably for their tea. He sounded off quite bitterly when he saw spots of blood that had not washed away completely. Ginger recalled that he sat there not daring to speak, not even to offer an apology. He was a new boy – a nozzer – and he didn't feel brave enough to try to explain. Ganges had that effect on new boys. Some of them never managed to handle the always present intimidation But nevertheless that SBA had no reason to browbeat a new recruit in that manner, moreso as that new recruit wasn't feeling too well.

After a while, alone in that cheerless room, he was called back by the dentist for a final check and then told to report back to his classes. As it was dinnertime he went straight to the Central Mess Galley for dinner.

Having had five teeth removed and many more jabbed and filled he had trouble eating. To bite with the new teeth was out of the question because the top of the teeth pushed up into raw gums where the previous teeth had just been extracted. He managed to cut up everything into very small pieces then place them almost down his throat.

With no consideration for the fact that he had almost every tooth jabbed, filled or removed, he was offered no painkillers or even excused doubling or strenuous activities, which made the blood flow. The bleeding continued for three days. That first night the bleeding covered half of one side of his pillow. He didn't report it. There was no point.

He was in a certain amount of pain and a lot of discomfort, in fact more discomfort than pain after that first night was over. He was also embarrassed to some degree and a little bit frightened. A little bit of sympathy wouldn't have come amiss; he was miserable that he didn't have anyone to confide in, not that would have eased his pain but it could have helped him feel a little better. He was on his own and it was doubtful if any of the others in the mess had even noticed. At the same time he was worried about talking to anyone in case he spat blood all over them. He couldn't talk properly with what seemed like a mouth full of something alien, so he figured his best bet was to say as little as possible and to keep his mouth closed most of the time.

The second morning there was more blood on the pillow. Being a new boy with only a few weeks under his belt he didn't say anything. He didn't know who to report to and, in any case it would have done no good. They had already got Batchelor, the assistant divisional officer on their case after that first afternoon in Hawke, and Leverett could be relied on to offer no sympathy or support.

Ginger was told to keep his new teeth in at all times and even to sleep with them. He didn't know what would happen if he took them out – whether they would bleed even more. He was afraid to remove them even to clean them. It was three days and after the bleeding had finally stopped, before he removed them for the first time.

That episode came back to him as clear as day as he sat eating his dinner, with his new teeth working a treat now that they had had several months to settle down.

In contrast to the heavy gun battery were the small arms. Small arms, as far as the boys were concerned, was a Lee Enfield .303 rifle. There were other small arms: divisional officers had pistols and instructors had Lanchesters. There was talk of some classes being introduced to a bren gun, although Ginger and the remainder of 49 mess never got to see one. Word was that some classes had a demonstration of dismantling a bren gun. Those that were lucky enough to have seen that demonstration, witnessed it on a table and in a classroom with their instructor showing them how clever he was by stripping it down to its individual component parts and then putting it back together again. No one ever got to fire a bren gun.

Only a very few classes ever got to see one apparently, and then it was only to satisfy their instructors ego: instructors who wanted to show off their skills at dismantling and re-assembling the weapon. They didn't impress anybody because no one knew what they were doing or if they were doing it correctly.

Ginger had spent some time with rifles and bren guns back home with the army cadets before joining up. He knew how to strip and put together bren guns and rifles but as that was not part of the small arms syllabus at Ganges that knowledge wasn't of any use to him. The vast majority of boys passed through Ganges without hearing the name or knowing what a bren gun was.

The rifle range was a different story. Ginger loved getting in there. The rifle range was just at the far side of the Gymnasia block and on the edge of the bank that led down to the foreshore. It was quite small and, considering the amount of people that used the place, it must have been crowded at times. The firing point was a concrete floor with a corrugated tin roof. It echoed, rattled and magnified the sounds and filled with cordite smoke when firing was in progress. Ahead lay about twenty-five yards of manicured lawn with the butts at the far end. The butts were simply targets affixed to their anchor points that had to be changed by hand after every shoot.

48

The lawn and the butts were open to the weather. There was a half sunken walkway along the right hand edge where one of the range staff GIs would walk to replace the targets and retrieve those used ones for analysis.

They mustered outside the range door one morning and all trooped inside. There was just space enough, standing at the back, to leave room for the people about to fire to lay down with their rifle.

Under Petty Officer Jury's leadership, rifles had been sloped, ordered, presented, changed, grounded and anything else you could think of. Now it was time to fire them.

As the first six took up their positions on the bit of matting that covered the concrete floor, the range chief went into his spiel.

'Always keep weapons pointed down the range.'

'Never load the magazine into the rifle until ordered to do so.'

'Do not pick up your weapon until ordered to do so.'

'When the magazine is shipped, do not close the bolt until ordered to do so.'

The same old stuff, trotted out with every successive class that passed through the place, day in and day out. At the same time, it needed saying and it needed adhering to. That first time on the range most of them had never seen a rifle close up before.

Ginger had the basics, he had done it before with the army cadets. He knew the routine. There wasn't much difference between the Army and Navy way and what little he didn't know he found easy to pick up. He didn't let on that he had done it before. Despite his knowledge he wasn't a very good shot and putting himself forward as a role model wouldn't have looked too good when he failed to hit the bullseye. Some of his classmates proved to be pretty good and a lot better than him that first time out, which, although he was happy for them, made him glad he hadn't told anyone how good he was!

They didn't spend a lot of time on that range although they had assessments each term. Everyone in the division had to shoot. The first time 61 and 62 classes competed Hawke won the competition. Hawke won the trophy; Hawke No. 8 section won the silver medal for highest score within the winning division and Hawke No. 7 section won bronze medals as runners-up. It was not recorded if the new boy's contribution helped in any way.

The officers and instructors scores were included in the competition results. They had their own sections within the competition but their score was part of the final result. The divisional officers with pistols, the assistant divisional officers and instructors with the Lanchester. Whether they did their shoot after the boys of their divisions had left, or at another time altogether, was not clear, because there was not enough room for everybody in that small tin-roofed area at the same time.

Leverett took them for one of their early sessions in the range and, for once, everything didn't have to be done his way. Throughout their time at Ganges he had always demanded that there was only one way to do things and that was his way.

But not on the range, they were quickly to find out. The reason was that he was left-handed and consequently he couldn't order things to be done his way. He made a competent job of firing a rifle left-handed himself, although to the boys his way looked awkward and cumbersome. He put the butt of the rifle into his left shoulder and sighted along the sights with his left eye. But that put the bolt on the wrong side and he had to reach across the rifle to work it with his left hand. As far as Ginger was aware there were no left-handers in 49 mess or if there were they managed to convert for the purposes of rifle firing.

At one particular session Ginger was feeling really low. Nothing had gone right for him. Long before they had ever got near the range on that day he was in the depths of frustration. Batchelor had been his usual self and just looking for anything slightly out of the ordinary to find fault with; Ginger attracted him like a magnet. Leverett had been ranting and raving as usual and Ginger had copped the bulk of his venom. Even Cyril Jury had singled him out for something he hadn't done and made him feel small and vulnerable.

By the time he reached the range he was really in the doldrums. Then, as he entered the range door, Fletcher, a chap he had befriended in the Annexe, hobbled past. Fletcher looked to be in a lot of pain.

'What's up with you, old mate?' Ginger enquired. 'Got a crack on the football field?'

'I've got a lump out of my leg,' Fletcher told him through gritted teeth.

'How'd you manage that, then?'

'Our bloody chief kicked me,' Fletcher replied, pulling his trouser leg out of his gaiter to show Ginger, revealing a wound about the size of an orange, all open and wet looking.

'Good grief, Fletch, you've got to go to the sick bay with that,' Ginger said, trying to attract the range chief's attention.

Fletcher grabbed his arm and pulled it down. 'No. Don't tell anyone!' he said, his face showing fear.

'But why ever not?' Ginger still wanted to catch the range chief's attention. 'You can't leave it like that.'

'No, no. I can't report it,' Fletcher replied, almost pleading. 'What can I tell them? I can't say that my instructor kicked me.'

He was right. Although acts of actual brutality did happen they were few and far between but they always went unreported. What could a mere boy do, faced with the denial of an instructor. Who would the authorities believe? What would be the repercussions? What would a boy's quality of life be like after reporting an instructor. Gingers friend had a serious leg wound and there was nothing either of them could do about it.

His mood changed from frustration through feeling sorry for himself, to dark depression. He hated the place. He hated the people. Then, as if fate had helped with the finishing touches to what was already a very bad day, Batchelor was waiting for them inside.

The thin-ringer always scowled. If there was ever any change to his facial features it was only when that scowl deepened. Ginger wiggled his way to the back of the congregated boys. The last thing he wanted was a confrontation with that nasty piece of work. He knew full well that something would be wrong if he was unfortunate enough to catch Batchelors eye.

Batchelor was at full power. He was on one of his ego trips. There were range staff GIs in there but Batchelor was running things. Why he was there was never explained. The staff didn't like being told how to run their department but Batchelor had the upper hand. He outranked them.

The boys stepped forward six at a time, to take their place on the firing line. Targets were placed at the butts and each rifleman was given a magazine with five rounds inside. Then the range chief would go into his usual spiel, with each successive line up, about not loading until he gave the order.

Almost as if on cue, Batchelor would interrupt the chief, just to remind everyone that he was still there and running things his way. He was just being disruptive; he was on one of his surges. There was a terrible atmosphere. Everyone hated him. After each six had fired their five rounds the targets were collected and Batchelor conducted an inquest on every one. The session dragged on painfully slow.

Ginger was in the last six to get called forward as he had kept well to the back. His mood hadn't lightened in the least. All the time he had been standing at the back he hadn't spoken to anyone. Watching and waiting all that time and listening to all that unnecessary waffle, just to allow Batchelor to enjoy himself, had really got to him. He was seething. Like everybody else, he wasn't about to say anything but inside he was almost at boiling point. How he hated that man. If he had a bayonet he might have stuck him with it and worried about the consequences later.

They lay on the matting and someone put a magazine with five rounds alongside them. Then, suddenly, he was aware of Batchelor striding along that sunken walkway. He was going to place the targets himself.

Got him!

Ginger's black mood turned to excitement. He was so excited that he forgot where he was temporarily. All he could think of was that Batchelor was going to step out in front of the butts to change targets. He would be out in the open and on his own – and that could be a good chance to shoot the bastard.

Luck lent him a helping hand. His magazine slipped down the matting a bit and by moving his body slightly and particularly his right arm, he could cover it out of sight and slip it quietly into the rifle. Then it would be simply a case of banging the bolt shut and firing as quickly as possible. He knew that he wasn't a very good shot and the entire episode had to hurried but he could hardly miss something the size of Batchelor, standing only twenty-five yards away. Plus he had a great incentive to make his one chance count. He could always say that he thought he heard someone give the order. He would worry about negligent discharge and charges of incompetence later, after all he was a boy under training.

As these thoughts raced through his mind and that magazine drew closer to its housing in the rifle, a shiny hobnailed boot placed itself on his fingers, not hard but firmly.

Ginger laid still, not daring to look up, and that boot remained unmoving on his fingers that were holding the magazine until Batchelor was back and out of danger.

With everything piling up on him that day; with his hatred of Batchelor; with the atmosphere in the range, Ginger really wanted to kill him and he would have made an attempt at it, but for that shiny boot.

He never learned who was on the other end of that shiny boot and the incident was never mentioned. Maybe they thought the action would have been justified but they didn't want to see a young lad go to prison – or worse – for doing something that they all wanted to do.

FIVE

Everything revolved around parades at Ganges. Very little was ever undertaken without some kind of parade first. Some of the minor happenings were referred to as musters and often someone would order 'fall in.' But, whatever the actual word used, it still amounted to the same thing: a parade.

The very first official naval words Ginger heard on his first day were, 'Fall in three deep.' That was from someone the Navy had sent to meet him and his fellow travellers as they alighted from the train at Ipswich station.

They hadn't joined up then. They hadn't even seen the place that they were heading for. Most of them, including Ginger, didn't know what Ganges was or where it was for that matter, yet here they were, accepting their first naval command almost as if they had been born to it – and that command started them onto their first parade right there, outside the station.

As the coach that had transported them from the station disgorged them into the Annexe, that command rang out again: 'Fall in three deep.'

Their second parade and they had only been in the place a matter of minutes! That parade was for the allocation of messes and beds within those messes. Ginger was assigned to Jellicoe Two mess and Chief Bumble. Then, after an hour or so in Jellicoe Two, Bumble ordered them to their third parade in as many hours, with the order, 'Fall in three deep outside, ready to march to the dining hall for supper.'

After supper there was no more parades that first day but there would be plenty more to follow as their time progressed. In fact the next morning, their first full day in the Navy, the parades intensified.

'Fall in, outside the mess.'

'Fall in, outside the sickbay.'

'Fall in, outside the clothing store.'

Fall in here, fall in there, fall in at the drop of a hat …. and so it went on.

For their first couple of days they didn't do any of the bigger parades. They didn't know about parades, big or small, but that all changed with the issue of their uniform and kit. Kit was issued on the first full day after their arrival. They trooped in one end of the clothing store and out the other with a full kit which had to be marked with the owner's name. It was not until that marking paint was dry did they get to try on their new clothes.

The following day they got their first taste of Navy uniform, although to start with it was only No.8s, the blue cotton work dress. Resplendent in their new No.8s, topped off with a black hat at one end and boots at the other, they were introduced to a parade in the real sense of the word. Or at least the way Ganges understood the meaning of the word.

Every one of them in the Annexe had arrived from home on the same day, so there was no one to learn from. There was no one to watch to see how it should be done. Everything had to be learnt from scratch via their mess instructor. In Ginger's case, Chief Bumble. Bumble was a patient man and, one step at a time they got the hang of parade drill. Until it was time for Divisions.

To start each day everybody paraded for Divisions. Each mess's occupants fell in, facing the small flagpole outside the divisional office. For the first few days the divisional officer would walk up and down the assembled ranks smiling a slight smile and nodding occasionally. Once in a while he would stop to speak to someone before continuing, with that slight smile still in place.

With Bumble teaching his class more and more each day and the other instructors doing the same with their classes, the boys soon got the hang of things, even those who had never done it before. Left turn, right turn and the ever so slightly more complicated, if somewhat wobbly, about turn were mastered. Then it felt time to introduce marching. Getting everyone to step off with the same foot while swinging the opposite arm took many hours to achieve until finally, it was deemed, they were ready to attempt their first march past.

A march past of sorts was accomplished. It was their first and it started them on their way, the first of many. The next obstacle was a repeat performance last thing at night. This time it was performed in a blue serge suit and called Evening Quarters. Although Evening Quarters was not as involved as Morning Divisions, it was still a parade and they had to be there.

Every possible reason that could be found to have them fall in and march somewhere was utilised. They were marched over to the barbers shop, which was a temporary set up in the NAAFI canteen on the end of the dining hall; they were marched over for the boxing tournament, in the same place; they were even marched over to the cinema.

The only parade that held even the slightest interest for them was the pay parade. Although the Navy pay system was fortnightly, Ganges boys were paid weekly. The Navy, in their wisdom, decreed that boys under training would be paid seventeen shillings and six pence per week. Out of that they would received the princely sum of five shillings at the weekly pay parade and a further five shillings could be allotted to their mum or placed in a Post

Office savings account. The remainder would be accounted for in a pay office ledger and used for kit replacement.

Five shillings didn't seem a lot but it was better than nothing and probably better than they would have got as a school-leaver at home, after paying mum housekeeping and the travelling fares that had to be contended with. The boys at Ganges had no housekeeping payments to concern themselves with and, as far as travelling went, they did that on two feet – and at the double. They looked forward to the pay parade and their five shillings. It wasn't a lot but it was all they would get until the same time the following week

As the days progressed and turned into weeks they wondered if there would ever be any let-up in those continual parades, musters and fall-ins.

Occasionally they would get a break in the otherwise monotonous routine of parades when they were summoned over to the main establishment for one reason or another. Although it was still a parade of sorts, marching over made a change. It was still marching but the scenery was different.

In the Annexe the routine for Divisions was always the same. They would start off facing the flagpole outside the divisional office and then turn left to face the Jellicoe messes. Then, as they were ordered to step off they turned left, almost at once, once again. That took them up alongside the Jellicoe and Beatty messes on their right and heading for the Dining Hall. A left turn at the Dining Hall and another left at the other side of the parade ground had them heading back toward the flagpole, past Cornwell and Tyrwhitt messes standing sentinel, empty and sounding hollow, looking exactly like the ones opposite.

Although they were not too impressed with leaving the comfort, such as it was, of familiar surroundings, the march over to 'The Main' made a change and gave them a glimpse of the world outside. It was only a short glimpse but it was better than nothing. It was a world that was quickly fading in their memories. There was so much to do in those early days that thoughts of the outside world were kept well to the back of their minds. Reminded once again and comparing to what they had endured since joining, what seemed a lot longer ago than it actually was, civilisation looked good.

As they left the Annexe road and crossed the main Shotley to Ipswich road, heading for the main gate, they passed a little corner shop similar to the one Ginger had worked in not so long ago. It brought back memories. There was a row of houses to their right next to the shop – a row of houses with real people in them. Real people not Navy people. What a refreshing change …. if only they had been allowed to stop and speak to them.

They made the trip over from the Annexe four times during their induction period. The first time to the main sickbay complex was in a blue suit. The next trip was to the dentist and that was made in their No.8s. The other two excursions, one for the mast test and the other for their swimming test, were undertaken in sports gear, probably for no other reason than both trips were made in the afternoon and everybody wore sports rig in the afternoon, whether involved in sport or not.

The common denominator for all four outings was – parade.

They were never very far away from a parade; they had either just completed one or were just about to immerse themselves in one. But on those four occasions it would have been a nice gesture to have allowed the boys a little leeway. After all they hadn't been given any shore leave and, what's more, all signs pointed to them not getting any in the foreseeable future.

In the leeway table boys were right at the back of the queue. So far back that when it became their turn there wasn't any left. The word was not even in an Annexe instructor's vocabulary.

With hindsight the boys now understood that Chief Bumble was one of the better instructors. It didn't take a genius to teach nozzers basic foot drill. No specialist knowledge was needed; simply referring back to their own basic training was enough. But what was required was patience. Not all new entry instructors had enough of it and it showed when their temper got the better of them.

Chief Bumble was not vicious, he was not violent and, as far as they could recall looking back, he had no personal axe to grind. He could be a bit snappy if the occasion demanded but that was only to be expected. When some of the other instructors were screaming forth and going red in the face on the parade ground, Bumble would sometimes mumble under his breath something about joining a monastery, when one of his charges was being particularly slow on the uptake.

Bumble had taught them to the best of his ability and he had taught them well, although to hear Batchelor, the assistant DO of Hawke tell it, when they first joined the main establishment, it was if they had never had a lesson in their lives before. But now they realised that Batchelor, being the way he is, they wouldn't have been good enough for him if they were the best drill squad in the world. Batchelor's opinions didn't mean much to them now they had got accustomed to his tyrannical ways, but his ever present interfering did.

Their last few parades, Divisions and their last Sunday Divisions, were accompanied by the Royal Marine Band, not the full band but a few drums – particularly the big drum – and a half dozen musicians. The object was to accustom them to marching to music. Then, one fine day, they marched off and out of the Annexe for good, never to return. But if they thought that their Annexe episode brought the curtain down on parades, they were sorely mistaken. The very next morning they were at it again.

In fact even earlier than that, because Batchelor was there to greet them straight after the dinner break. They had marched out of the Annexe, full of happiness and anticipation, just prior to dinnertime and then, straight after dinner, he appeared to begin his reign of interfering.

It was their introduction to Batchelor and he made it quite clear from the very first moment, that he wasn't there to be liked.

There was no way they could have known it but they were earmarked for an easy afternoon in their mess, just unpacking their kitbags and stowing things away into their new lockers. That was the plan. Although they were not aware of it – Batchelor had other ideas.

Chief Bumble had convinced them that life would be much easier when they got over to the main establishment then, their very first parade, which was an unnecessary parade anyway, was worse than anything they had endured during their Annexe period.

Before dinner that day they had never even heard of Batchelor, but after dinner it was a different story. Having suffered a couple of hours of stomping up and down the Hawke Division colonnade, purely to satisfy his ego, they were never likely to forget him. The name of Batchelor would be imprinted on their brain forever.

The next morning they experienced their first Divisions in the main establishment. All two thousand boys fell in, in three ranks, in their divisions and by messes, facing Nelson Hall, the drill shed, which was on the west side of the parade ground. The senior classes were at the front and seniority decreased as others took their place behind them, forever decreasing down toward the back. Being the new boys their place was right at the back and not very far from Hawke Division.

They were like lost sheep as they congregated in the recess on the east edge of the parade ground. A recess that was created by Collingwood Division having been built at right angles to Hawke and set back from the parade ground several feet. The long edge of Collingwood was parallel to the edge of the parade ground.

Petty Officer Jury was there to make sure they got to the correct position. He had already detailed off Shavers to be their marker. When the parade Chief GI called for markers, Shavers knew where he had to be and eventually the new boys of Hawke 49 mess formed their three ranks on Shavers, their corner post.

Shavers was distinctive, partly because of his extra inches in height and partly because he always said *Thee and Thou*. He was distinctive and stood out and that got Ginger to scrutinising some of the other mess occupants. There were two Farmers and both entirely different from each other. One was thin and dark haired with a pointed nose who hardly ever spoke, and the other was Daisy the badge boy. Daisy was small and fair-haired with freckles and a likeable sort of chap. There were two Moors. One was a short, stocky ginger-haired lad and the other was tall with white hair and a pale complexion. Then there was the two Davis'. JF was one and he looked a lot like Stan Laurel of Laurel and Hardy fame. The other was Welsh Dai. He was heavy-set, with dark features and black hair. JF was a Midlander and Dai spoke slowly and deeper, with a strong Welsh accent.

Ginger got to thinking that any time two people became associated in some way, almost like a double act, they always appeared to be completely opposite to each other. Their mess instructors were a good example: Leverett was an acting petty officer and wore square rig the same as the boys while Cyril Jury wore fore and aft rig of an established petty officer. Leverett was tall and thin; Jury carried a little more weight and was not quite as tall.

The divisional officer, Cassidy, was fairly tall with a very light, almost pasty complexion and fair hair, whereas Batchelor, the assistant divisional officer, was short and with a much darker skin tone and dark hair. Even back in the Annexe, the buzz-spreaders, Lowley and Shiny Black, were opposites.

The attitude of the 'odd-couples' and their personalities always seemed to be absolutely opposed to each other as well. Leverett was arrogant and nasty while Jury was approachable and smart. Cassidy rarely spoke a word to the boys but Batchelor would never shut up or leave them alone.

Their first Divisions in The Main were carried out smoothly and without mistakes. That was quite a feat as none of them had any idea. They were helped along a bit by two thousand boys ahead of them, showing them the way and what to do and how to do it, so all they had to do was watch points and follow-the-leader. PO Jury was there in any case, to keep them on the straight and narrow.

At the other end of the day, Evening Quarters was, by comparison, a piece of cake. It was performed in their blue suit and, really just amounted to a head count to see that everyone was accounted for. As far as the boys were concerned it signalled the last parade of the day.

After their first Evening Quarters the rest of the day was easy. The latest batch of nozzers always joined the main establishment on a Wednesday, just as Ginger's recruitment had done that very day, and Wednesday night was cinema night. With their last outing to the parade ground over, the next bit was quite pleasant as they trooped back to the mess before making their way to the gymnasia block and No.1 gym for a night at the pictures.

All the gym benches – that in many future visits they would be forced to raise and lower above their heads, four to a bench, in strength building exercises, or as they saw it strength *sapping* exercises – were lined up in rows across the gym floor, leaving a pathway down the centre and facing the screen.

The benches were not over comfortable with no backs to them but two thousand boys could handle the slight discomfort, after all it was better than a session in the school block or chasing up and down the parade ground. As time went on they were to learn that a really soul destroying form of punishment was to be denied access to the weekly picture show. It may not have sounded much to the people back home but minor things took on major proportions at Ganges and became very important. Back home, missing a trip to the pictures wouldn't have rated very highly, but being denied the Ganges picture show, their only bit of light relief where they could lose themselves for a couple of hours each week and be alone if they wanted to be without an ever present instructor in close attendance, could bring some of them close to tears.

Being new boys they had no idea what 'picture routine' entailed for their first time. In keeping with every other happening at Ganges, they were not enlightened until the commencement of the actual event. But the moment the lights went down and the old Pathé cockerel appeared on the screen, the rustling started as bars of nutty, packets of sweets and cigarettes appeared from the depths of blue serge jumpers.

By the time the newsreel had ended and they were into the 'Good Old Fred' cartoon, the air was thick with tobacco smoke. The nozzers were a bit on the envious side but consoled themselves with the fact that they didn't know. But they made a mental note that from the next Wednesday on things would be different.

If the weekly picture show, where they could lose themselves in the semi darkness and forget routines and instructors for a couple of hours, was the highlight of their week then, surely, boats, boating and scrubbing out boats on a Saturday morning was the low point. It certainly was for Ginger and he knew he was not alone.

Some of the boys absolutely loved being on the river and several of them qualified as sailing coxswains. There was a sailing club, and occasionally the club members were allowed away for a weekend sailing and camping out. Ginger wanted none of it. Boating and river work was never pleasant for him. PO Leverett probably triggered his dislike. From their earliest associations with the water it had always been Leverett who was in charge. Leverett was a downright nasty man and, although he appeared to enjoy being down on the river his enthusiasm was not contagious. His attitude seemed to be that he was there to enjoy himself and he wasn't interested in anyone else's feelings.

The boat jetty was an L shaped wooden pier that stuck out into the river, just opposite the bottom of Faith, Hope and Charity, the stone steps that led from the southern end of the quarterdeck and wardroom to the foreshore road. The long leg of the L turned east and ran parallel to the coastline and was the starting point for all boating activity, whether it was whalers or cutters, with oars or under sail.

Boats from visiting ships would come alongside there and the Ganges liberty boat sailed from there, taking shore leave parties over the river and its other harbour duties.

With Leverett at the helm, metaphorically speaking as well as in fact, they knew enough to man either type of boat and rig for pulling or sailing, long before they ever set foot in one.

There were two types of boat for the boys to master: the whaler, pointed at both ends, was the smaller of the two at 27 feet long and was manned by a crew of five with a coxswain at the tiller. The five oarsmen were situated three on the starboard side and two to port. But the bugbear for them was the 32 feet long cutter which carried twelve oars, six on each side. The cutter had a straight stern. Leverett liked to get them into the cutter and they figured that the only reason was because it was harder work for them, although it made him happy.

All the groundwork instruction on boats was done in the seamanship block with models, or on the 'dry land cutter' that was set on a concrete base outside. So when it came time for the real McCoy down on the river there was no reason for any further delay. As soon as they would arrive on the boat jetty his instant order was, 'First twelve man the boat, remainder man the falls.' He was always eager to be getting on the water and no dithering or time wasting would be tolerated. He wanted every minute of the session to be used to the full. Although it was never put into words, his attitude appeared to be: *You've done the theory now put it into practice.*

Leverett enjoyed sailing but it was never a sedate drift along with time to look at the ships coming and going over the Harwich side. With him in control it was continually changing tack or going about, which meant extra work for the boy crew. Sometimes when he was in one of his occasional better moods he would take them on a racing trip where he would get the full wind in the sails and have the lee side gunwales over so far that water was lapping into the boat.

But where he really came into his own was with the pulling crew. Pulling was another ridiculous Navy term for rowing. Propelling a 32 foot cutter through the water with a dozen fifteen year olds as crew and using large wooden oars that weighed as much as some of the smaller boys, must have been a sight to behold, and one that the merchant seamen who sometimes watched from their Harwich side docked ships, were glad they didn't have to do.

There was never any encouragement or praise from Leverett. If they struggled to reach his expected standard at any stage, they would have to do it over and over until he was satisfied or, if the allocated time came to an end, some other reminder would be substituted – like an extra kit inspection in their own limited free time, or extra drill instead of the weekly picture show. Alternatively if somehow they managed to meet the standard he had set them, he would growl: 'Well, if you can do that, I expect better next time.'

There was no pleasing the man. He would enjoy a period out on the river and it wouldn't even occur to him what hardship he may have caused others. He made no concession to the smaller of them who had trouble controlling the big heavy oars; he expected them to keep up with their bigger and stronger classmates.

Another element that he introduced them to, almost from the start, was what he called his 'up-for-ten' order. This entailed them digging their oars in deep with short fast strokes. The idea was designed to get a boat moving quickly from a standing start for pulling races at boating competitions but he used it as another lever to make them suffer even more.

He would shout: up-for-five, ten or even twenty on occasion, depending how sadistic his mood happened to be. It started almost from their first lesson and before any of them had got to grips properly with the boat, oars and river.

As time progressed and they were entered into pulling races and competitions, it was great to feel the boat lift out of the water as they powered away from the starting line. But in those early days, when everything was still new to them, Leverett would use his up-for-ten command simply to watch them struggle. It was not unusual when, after a gruelling session in a pulling cutter, he would order an up-for-ten for no reason whatsoever, on the way back to the boat jetty and when aching limbs could hardly take any more, only to have to order 'hold water' to take the way off the boat to prevent it crashing at full speed into the jetty framework.

There was one occasion when he was out on the river with 62 class, his own class and things were not going to his liking. Shilling, one of the oarsmen was being even more cack-handed than usual and getting into all kinds of trouble with his oar and keeping in stroke with the others. Leverett snatched the tiller out of its mounting in the top of the rudder and hit Shilling a fearsome blow on the head with it. On that occasion his temper got the better of him but even then there was no remorse.

Ray Leeward, who was on the opposite side to Shilling, lifted his oar clear of the water and leaned over to help Shilling, who was in a crumpled heap in the bottom of the boat. Leverett's response was to wave the tiller bar threateningly close to Leeward's face and bellowed, 'Leave him there!'

Shilling was unconscious in the bottom of the boat and making gurgling noises in the back of his throat but Leverett ignored him. He wasn't the most popular boy in the mess but nevertheless he didn't deserve that kind of treatment. He should never have been hit, particularly by someone whose role it was to take care of boys under their control – and certainly not that hard and with a length of wood. Leverett was such a threatening presence that the incident went unreported.

Before they had been there very long and well before their first leave was due, they had had so much training under Leverett that six crews from Hawke Division were entered for the Style Cutter Competition on the river. They were told, by the divisional officer, that all six crews had qualified with a high scoring average and that Leverett's own crew topped 75 points. The nearest division after Hawke was nine points behind, he told them.

It was not so much that Leverett taught them well, although he knew his stuff but more a case of them being bullied to such a degree that they were afraid of failing. They didn't strive to do well to please or for personal satisfaction. They sweated and strained out of fear of the man. Aching limbs and almost collapsing brought on by near exhaustion, was preferable to incurring his full wrath. They were afraid of the man but they were more afraid of not meeting the high standard he set for them.

There was no personal praise or word of congratulation for the boys even though they gave their best. Undoubtedly there were celebrations in the POs Mess among the competing coxswains and also in the wardroom between divisional officers, with a few side bets to be settled but for the boys that had done the work and given a hundred per cent effort, there was nothing.

Even when Cassidy, the divisional officer, made one of his rare appearances to relay the results to them, he did it in a matter-of-fact manner, almost as if he couldn't be bothered and didn't want to be there. He read from a paper, what appeared to be a prepared statement and with no emotion. He singled Leverett out for a special mention and a few boys from other messes, who didn't know him, clapped politely but from the inhabitants of 49 mess there was a sullen silence. Even Leverett never mentioned his accolade again. He must have known how they felt.

A few days later Cassidy was at it again with another of his congratulatory speeches. This time it was for the Piping Competition winners. Both the establishment's top placings went to boys from 49 mess. This time there was no reflected glory for Leverett to wallow in.

By the greatest of coincidences it was Shilling who won the day with Ray Leeward a very close second, by the merest of margins. Below them was a big gap to the next placed competitor. A nice trick of fate, as they were the two involved with the tiller incident on the river and this time Leverett had nothing to do with it.

This time, after mumbling on, Cassidy made an attempt at being jovial. Someone must have told him that his last speech was too formal and abrupt. Either that or he had been on the wardroom gin.

'Summer leave is almost upon us,' he told them. 'We shall soon be making a beeline for the main gate. Don't start to let your standards slip now. It's only three weeks to go and you can always get your long leave stopped!'

Some attempt at joviality. The man had no idea how to talk to people. That kind of comment they expected from Batchelor, the assistant DO. They would have accepted it from him and probably not even have noticed. But for that man to stand in front of them, allegedly to tell them how proud he was of their achievements, having accepted the plaudits from all and sundry about how well *his* division had done in the Style Cutter and Piping Competitions, then to more-or-less state that they had better watch themselves or he would stop their leave, was going too far. They had heard enough from him. He must have been in great demand in the wardroom as an after dinner speaker. His social chit-chat and ready wit would keep them rolling in their seats all night. How he ever got to be selected for a divisional officer at Ganges beggared belief. It was apparent that he hadn't volunteered.

Looking back at those events now, it was easy to view them with the aid of rose tinted spectacles and overlook the hardships they had endured. It was hard and they were green. It had cost them a lot to give of their best. Maybe there was just a touch of achievement felt privately and maybe even just a passing thought of satisfaction in knowing Leverett hadn't beaten them. But they felt no elation whatsoever. It was just another milestone passed.

Another unpleasant task concerning boats was the scrubbing out sessions. This was a Saturday morning task. All boats were hoisted up on their davits, along the length of the boat jetty and the boys were detailed off to scrub out the boats used by their own division. Hawke Division cutter was the first one on the corner.

Each boat would have four or five boys to scrub out the inside. A bucket of sea water would be dredged out of the river directly underneath the boat and then hands, numb with cold even during the summer months, would scrub the wooden thwarts (seats) and the entire interior, right down to the bottom.

Leverett showed them what to do the first time and, naturally, he had to make thing as difficult as possible. Four or five times that bucket had to be dropped into the water and then hoisted back up, which was no easy task. Each time the full bucket came up it had to be handed to him. He then threw it into the boat screaming for more water until there was a good depth of water throughout. He then ordered the scrubbing party into the boat, to kneel on the thwarts that went from side to side and reach down into the cold water and scrub the insides and bottom.

But after that first time his enthusiasm for scrubbing out waned. It wasn't much fun for him to stand on the jetty watching, he wanted to be involved. As soon as the water throwing period was over his interest left him and after that first session he was hardly ever seen on a Saturday morning again. There was usually a petty officer or a chief on the jetty somewhere but as the boys didn't know who it was, they were left on their own to get on with it.

The boys only had their boots to wear so they didn't want too much water inside the boat, for fear of getting their boots or their feet wet. They had no Wellington boots. As time progressed it was decreed that they wear plimsoles in boats but for those first couple of scrubbing sessions they had to try to keep their boots dry.

After that first session with Leverett where they just had to follow his orders and another when they were left to their own devices, Ginger came up with a solution. His idea was to get one bucket of river water up and stand it carefully in the bottom of the boat. Then just scrub the thwarts, which were plain wood and could get dirty. The remainder of the internal was painted white and a quick wipe with damp cotton waste was all that was required. After that it was simply a case of looking busy and keeping as warm as possible, until just before the end of the session when the water was poured carefully through the plug hole to look as if it was running from the bottom of the boat. This new plan spread quickly through 49 mess and unless they were closely supervised, was adopted by whoever was doing the scrubbing. Their boat always looked as clean, with only ten minutes work, as any other. That scheme was never tumbled.

The alternative to scrubbing out boats on a Saturday morning was scrubbing out the Central Mess Galley, or at least Hawke section of it. There was little to choose between the two tasks except, of course, the CMG water was a lot warmer.

Once again Ginger landed on his feet, although to start with it was more by luck and good fortune than any planning or judgement on his part. He always marvelled at how the front-runners managed to squabble and almost fight each other to get picked for the jobs first. They were always eager to please and, hopefully, score a few points with 'Sir'. The first time he was detailed he wasn't quite sure what would happen. Some of them had done it before and the moment PO Jury mentioned CMG party, there was a mad scramble, almost as he spoke.

Sweaty Gillette and Dereham, closely followed by their hangers-on, blustered and elbowed their way to the front and instantly there were no jobs left. Ginger was at the back without a job. They moved off and he followed the crowd, led by Jury, to the dining hall. All the time he was debating whether to peel off somewhere along the way but deciding against it because there was nowhere else to go.

Inside was a hub of activity with other division members getting started in their sections. Hawke section was the first one inside the door down at the far end. Ginger couldn't understand why his classmates were so keen to work in there. Other than scoring a few points, which was unlikely, there was nothing to be gained as far as he could see. There was no prospect of a cup of tea or an odd sandwich or two. They were too far from that part of the galley and the cooks were too busy preparing the midday dinner to entertain any such notions, plus there was a lot of hard work to be completed before dinner. No. His *'green coat production'* was a much better plan and it was coming along nicely, thread by thread.

His first order of business was to get out of that place as soon as possible, before Jury roped him in to help. He grabbed a cooking pot that was similar in shape and size to their milk and cocoa fanny back in the mess and high-tailed it back to the familiar surrounds of Hawke block where he spent the better part of three hours polishing that pot with bluebell polish. It wasn't dirty or in need of polishing in the first place. It was a sunny morning and he was quite happy sitting out in the sun. There was no sign of Leverett or Batchelor.

Armed with that knowledge, he spent many a happy Saturday morning sitting outside Hawke block polishing sometimes no more than a pot lid while the front-runners and tough guys worked hard and sweated away in the dining hall. It was entirely their own fault. They volunteered and pushed themselves forward. Ginger was quite happy doing next to nothing and no one seemed to object. In any case it was much preferable to scrubbing out boats with freezing cold fingers.

SIX

Leave was very important. All Ganges boys looked forward to leave. There was precious little else to look forward to. It only came around every three months or so and very few of them ever got outside in between those perimeters. Leave was lingering in the back of everyone's mind most of the time. Any little incident could trigger a memory and bring it back sharply into focus. The sight of a dog could do it and had done so on occasion for Ginger. Just the sight of someone walking their dog would remind him of his dog back home. That in turn would get him to thinking about how long it would be before he would be heading that way again.

Most Ganges boys had a leave-chart, a kind of a home made three-month calendar. After returning from leave, a new chart would be produced as soon as possible to cover the period up to the next leave. Some boys made theirs from their own writing pad but most charts were compiled from paper pilfered from the school. At the earliest opportunity a sheet of paper would be spirited away and divided into the required number of squares – one square for each day until the next leave. A term was usually around 100 days, or a few more, and was easy enough to work out with the aid of a school ruler when the schoolie wasn't looking.

Back in the mess, charts were kept out of sight in the little brown attaché case. That was the only bit of privacy they had at Ganges. Even Batchelor or Leverett never touched that little bit of personal property although they would quite happily root through lockers without a seconds hesitation. On the chart each day was religiously crossed off as days turned into weeks and weeks nibbled away at the term. To start with it was soul destroying to see just a few crosses in isolation on an almost blank and empty chart. But as time progressed it seemed to move a bit faster, particularly as they had plenty of other things to occupy their minds. Conversely, the last three or four squares appeared to pass very slowly as their imminent leave took over their entire thinking process.

On leave morning all thoughts of leave charts were erased from the mind as quickly as the now redundant chart was consigned to the rubbish bin. At that stage other urgent matters occupied their thoughts and their time.

Having awoken to 'Tiddley Charlie' over the Tannoy, those that were still in bed – and there were few enough of them – jumped out to get their bedding stacked up for the last time for three weeks. Then their priority was to get the mess clean enough to assuage Batchelor and get breakfast over and done with.

Most of 49 mess were already in their best blue suit when they trooped over for breakfast, and those that were not changed as soon as breakfast was over. Ginger could see no reason to put on his blue uniform that early. After all they were old hands now, they had been on leave before and they knew the routine well enough.

Daisy, their badge boy, had changed as soon as the lights were turned out the night before. A few more had followed suit and that little gathering sat in the airing room playing cards all through the night.

Ginger was as keen as any of them to be getting out of the place as soon as possible but he could see no reason to go without a nights sleep. He couldn't see how there was anything to be gained from that, plus, he figured that there was no point in being tired all the first day of his leave through having been up all night. He figured to sleep in Ganges time and be fully awake and fresh when it became his turn for them to let him out of there. He was as keen as any of them to be getting a move on but he couldn't see how going without sleep would help anything. Excited they might be but he could contain his excitement until he was on that train and out of their sight. In any case, the people with furthest to go would get out first and his group 'The Norwich Group' wouldn't get away for at least a couple of hours after breakfast had finished; they knew that, they had done it all before.

Nevertheless many people from other divisions and undoubtedly Hawke as well, had begun to congregate outside Nelson Hall long in advance of their departure time. Everyone had been assigned a group and each group was allocated a time to muster inside Nelson Hall. Many of them had been through it before but they still felt compelled to hang around.

They were excited. Excitement was in the air. The place had lost its foreboding feel. Although they were old hands now, they couldn't help but wallow in the relaxed atmosphere. It was all around them. Everyone could sense it. They were about to go on leave. They were about to get out of the place. They could almost taste the freedom. Boys were strolling around on the parade ground, something they would never have dreamed of doing the day before.

Ginger was as happy as any of them to be getting out of that gate. He wasn't too worried about getting home as many of them seemed to be, he just wanted to get away outside and shake Ganges off for three whole weeks. The atmosphere was very relaxed but he didn't throw caution to the wind like most of them appeared to have done. Although there were no instructors to be seen, apart from a few that were engaged in marshalling lines of boys through the check-points in Nelson Hall, or directing boys onto buses and full buses away to Ipswich station, he wasn't about to take any unnecessary risks.

He decided to keep well out of the way. He knew what time his group would be called for and, in any case, they sang out for the various groups over the Tannoy as it was time for them to muster. There was nothing to be gained by getting over there any earlier. In any case Batchelor or Leverett might put in an appearance and that could well mean a trip over the mast in their best blue suit for some poor unfortunate. Ginger had had first hand experience of both of them in the past and he wasn't ready for any of their interference this close to leave. Either one of them would take pleasure in ordering a trip over the mast or making someone double around the parade ground, for no other reason than to remind everyone that they were there and still in charge. He was surprised that others from Hawke hadn't taken a little more heed. Maybe the excitement had blown everything else out of their head.

Most of 49 mess had left before it was his turn to go. They were headed in the opposite direction, toward London's Liverpool Street Station. From there they dispersed through the other London main-line stations before leaving for their destinations; some up to the midlands and the north, some to the south coast and some through Kent. Daisy lived in Kent, not far from Canterbury.

Word had it that the London stations had shore patrols, so those boys travelling in that direction were well behaved until their train took them clear of London. There were no such restrictions for the Norwich Group. There were no patrols at Norwich station. So, as soon as the other compartments had been checked to ensure there were no officers or instructors travelling on the same train, badges and cap tallies would appear to accompany the turned-back cuffs and flat-aback-hats.

Ginger recalled that he was taken by surprise on their first leave when everyone – except him – turned themselves into salt encrusted veterans by the liberal application of badges, just as soon as the train wheels started to turn. But now, with a bit of time under their belts, such as it was, he thought that kind of practice would have died out with the nozzers tag that they were so keen to lose.

It crossed his mind that those boys adorning themselves would in all probability not remember what they had sewed on for that last leave and he wondered how they would explain away a sudden career change, commensurate with the current badges, bearing in mind that all promotions and change of branch had happened within the last three months since they were home last – and them still just hovering around their sixteenth birthday.

There had been talk of a young lad, waiting for his train at one of the London stations, who got talking to a chap in the station bar, where he should never have been in the first place and explaining about his badges and all the foreign ports he had visited. They had a long chat and his new friend seemed very interested in the lad and tales of time spent abroad. He wished the boy well as they parted to catch their respective trains. Later, with leave over, the boy returned to Ganges reverted to his lowly boy second-class status and minus his new found promotions. He was summoned to his divisional office where he was met by his divisional officer and a petty officer that looked vaguely familiar.

Then the penny dropped. That three-badge petty officer was his 'friend' from the station on leave morning! Between them, the DO and the PO read that boy *The Riot Act, The Articles of War* and the third verse from *The Halls of Montezuma* as well probably, but they got his attention. From then on it was no more illicit badges or tall stories for him, he assured them.

Sitting there on the train, speeding its way toward Norwich, Ginger recalled that story and that, in turn, prompted him to recall one of his own from a previous leave.

Someone had given him a British Railways cap tally and, although he wasn't very keen, he allowed it to be put onto his hat. At that time he didn't know where the cap tally had come from but he remembered that he was idiot enough to leave it on his hat. When he arrived home, the first person he bumped into was an old acquaintance he had known for a couple of years and who worked for the railways. Ginger had stepped straight into the trap he had been advising others to avoid. He was cornered. With a glass of brown ale in his hand in the pub. He wiggled his way out from under by spinning a line about how he had been seconded to help the rail people on their train ferries at Harwich because he knew all about seamanship and they didn't.

His friend, who was a year or two older and had worked for the railways for some time, said he didn't know of naval people on the ferries and thought it a bit odd, so did the others who were listening at the village pub bar. They told him that rail ferry crewmen wore a navy blue wool jersey and a navy seaman's hat with the cap tally like his but they were not Navy and they didn't employ Navy seamen. Ginger was well out of his depth; he had no idea what he was talking about. He rather hoped they didn't know either but apparently they did, or at least, they had a better idea of the situation than he did. He didn't know if there were train ferries running out of Harwich, although, apparently there was. He certainly didn't know where they ran to.

Luckily that was never brought up. He was just making it up as he went along. It must have sounded like a load of old twaddle and he was fortunate that they took him at face value and no one bothered to check his story out.

After that near miss that cap tally came off as soon as he got to his house. The following day he came up with an explanation that it had only been a temporary assignment and it was over now. He had been ordered back to Ganges when his draft leave was over. It sounded reasonable. After all, many of them had been on temporary assignment a few months back during the floods.

How the others on the train got away with it he really didn't know. Some of them almost turned themselves into a Christmas tree, with so many decorations festooned all over themselves. Once was enough for him. He'd had a few sticky moments and had to wiggle like never before. That was his one and only time trying to be something he wasn't.

For his first leave way back in August, Ginger remembered that he had felt subdued. The mates he had left behind seemed just the same, after all it was only three months, although to him it seemed a whole lot longer.

He recalled that he sat around the house for the bulk of his first day home, almost as if he was afraid to go out. Being a village, he knew almost everyone but somehow he felt different. Not better, superior, or inferior for that matter, just different. The nearest he could come to putting a tag on it was alien. After being at Ganges, albeit for only three months, he felt that somehow things had changed and he no longer belonged.

Toward the end of the afternoon he ventured outside and took a walk around the village. It was only a small place and the lot could be covered in about twenty minutes, or half an hour if he stopped to speak with anyone. He knew the route perfectly well because it wasn't that long ago that he was delivering newspapers and groceries to the same people that he now felt out of touch with. People treated him the same as always but he found difficulty in knowing how to respond. Thanks to Ganges and in particular Petty Officer Leverett and Batchelor the assistant divisional officer, in a matter of only nine months he had lost the art of conversation.

He had never been the shy and retiring type but at the same time he had never been the pushy front-runner type either. He had always fitted in comfortably.

Now, looking back to that first leave, he recalled a feeling of isolation. He had felt like a stranger in the place where he had spent all his early life. His school chums that he had left behind treated him no differently on the surface at least, although he sensed there was a slight atmosphere; some made little sarcastic jibes about his appearance and, in particular his short haircut, others gave off signs of envy. He certainly envied them their freedom, bearing in mind that his was now tied up for a very long time. Somehow he felt a stranger among friends and that, in some indefinable way, he had outgrown them.

Now, six months later, it was a different story and that self-consciousness was gone. Where his father wanted him to wear his uniform at every opportunity during that first leave, now it was rolled up and consigned to the top of the wardrobe as soon as he stepped inside the door and it remained there until the morning of his return to Ganges. It appeared that his father, who had never been anywhere due to his reserved work with dairy-farm animals, was secretly proud of him and wanted to bask in some kind of reflected glory. But enough was enough for Ginger. Having been allowed to wear nothing but uniform all day, every day since his last leave, he wasn't about to wear it when there was no reason to do so. He was an old hand now, with more than half of his Ganges year behind him but he had to keep his wits about him. Like when the often asked question arose: 'What's it like?'

He had to be as positive as possible with his answer, while at the same time non-committal. He didn't know what it was like. He hadn't really found that out. He still had to go to sea and he couldn't embarrass himself by admitting that he wasn't a real sailor yet. Some of the local lads that he knew had been called up for National Service during his absence and during the intervening months, they had finished their basic training and had done a spell in Korea or Germany. They were old hands and had seen action. Ginger could hardly tell them that during that same period all he had seen was Ipswich station and Ganges!

Being a village, most of the travelling had to be done by bicycle. The two shops and the two pubs were within easy walking distance but to venture further afield a bicycle made life a lot easier. There were one or two cars in the village but they were few and far between and Ginger's dad didn't own one. A local branch-line railway ran to Norwich two and sometimes three times a day but with only three pounds for the entire three weeks leave too many trips on that, nice as it would have been, was out of the question.

Ginger's bicycle was a godsend. He had owned one from a very early age. Then he'd had the grocers bike with the iron basket attached to the front. He had travelled miles on that old bike without the aid of any gears and pushing a large basket of groceries. He had also been an up-and-coming speedway rider with his own track bike. Cycle speedway was a big thing in his neck of the woods, as was its mechanised elder brother. Norfolk people loved their speedway.

The cycle speedway team never quite made it to league status and when Ginger left the whole thing appeared to flounder. The team demise was probably due to most of the members being around the same age and finding motorbikes and girlfriends. A couple of years later National Service required their attention.

He recalled an incident way back when he had first joined Hawke Division from the Annexe. It was early days, maybe only their second or third day in their new home, when Petty Officer Leverett demanded in that way of his: 'Can anyone ride a bike?'

Ginger, eager to please, thought that this would be a good way to get noticed and score a few points. He naively thought that the town and city dwellers wouldn't have any experience of bicycles. On the other hand he, with his years of riding behind him and having been a cycle speedway rider, would be an ideal candidate. He went to step forward but was almost knocked over as Dereham and Sweaty Gillette and company shoved and elbowed their way to the front in their desperation to get noticed.

Leverett selected his squad and they stood smugly grinning at those that had not been picked. Ginger was put out by the fact that he hadn't been chosen. He figured that he could hold his own against any of them. If only they had seen him on the track back home blasting away from the tapes and taking corners like a seasoned professional. Now they would never know. Maybe this could have been something to make him stand out from the crowd, something to make the Navy proud of him. He couldn't swim when he joined up and he was afraid of the mast, but this he would have been good at.

But riding a bike was just Leverett's concession at humour. All those smug, grinning, pushy know-alls spent the entire afternoon picking up paper and rubbish from the playing fields.

Ginger did learn a valuable lesson from that episode though and that was simply: never volunteer. He learned his lesson and remembered it well. He hadn't volunteered although he had tried to. That was the only time. He never volunteered again.

The hangers-on brigade never did quite get the message. Leverett tried that same routine a couple of more times as the weeks went by and still they leapt and scrambled their way to the front. They had already had a taste of what was in store for volunteers but each time someone who could ride a bike was called for, they made a point of being at the head of the queue, not that there ever was a queue after that first time.

Occasionally, on days when they were duty division, the Chief Buffer, or someone from the Buffers Party, would ask for anyone who could ride a bike and still the same old faces would fight to get noticed. The vast majority of 49 mess were quite happy to stand still and do nothing; they had learned enough from their first encounter with that particular question. They had cottoned on to such an extent that when the question arose, they tried to leave a clear passage so Dereham, Sweaty Gillette & Co. could reach the front with ease. They seemed to be the only ones not understanding the situation. Naturally the remainder of the mess were quite prepared to leave them in the dark.

Sometimes the PTIs or an occasional schoolie would trot out the old formula, presumably thinking that they were the first to try it on or, maybe, that the boys hadn't heard it before. Several times the class had got away to an early stand-easy leaving Gillette and his cronies sweeping the gym floor or putting charts or books away in the school classroom.

After a while Dereham didn't appear as keen. He noticeably held back when bike riders were called for. Someone must have put him wise. He never would have figured it out for himself.

Bikes had played a significant part in Gingers early life and, on his leaves from Ganges, they still came in very handy. Villages, being villages, were isolated communities, set apart from each other and bicycles were the most common way of getting around.

Gingers village was on the main Norwich to Fakenham road and had a train station. It was also on a bus route, so they were luckier than most. But many of the nearby villages had neither, so a bicycle – or a car for the more fortunate – was essential for getting off the main routes. Ginger liked getting out into the countryside of an evening because he had no trouble getting served in the pubs. Country pubs didn't get much passing custom and no-one ever queried his age, like they would have done in the city pubs. Country people were much friendlier than city folk anyway and particularly so in that part of the country. He had never been questioned in his two village pubs either, although both landlords would have known how old he was from his earlier occupation of newspapers and grocery deliveries.

The pub by the river, The Bridge, was owned by a former matelot, Jack. Yorkie Jack was more interested in how he was getting on and how the Navy was changing than how old he was. Jack was a nice bloke and, being ex-Navy, he would have spotted any rogue badges, which was another good reason for Ginger not to have joined in the 'instant promotion stampede'. Thankfully he wasn't there on the day of the British Railways cap tally incident.

By coincidence, The Kings Head, the other pub about two hundred yards away, was also run by a man called Jack. Jack Button was a farmer; he wasn't up on things naval although, maybe, he should have been seeing as how his son Kenny was in the Navy. Jack would often talk about Kenny, although he hadn't much idea what he was saying. Kenny was away for the year that Ginger was at Ganges, so they never met. Apparently Kenny was expecting to be rated leading seaman, Jack told him. That meant that he would be 'killit' and like a ships foreman, he explained solemnly. Ginger figured out that Kenny had told his dad 'killick' but Jack didn't understand. He also stated that Kenny had a big badge on his arm 'that looked like a spider's web'. Ginger instantly had visions of a radar plotter's badge but, from photos produced by a pround parent, he deduced that it was a torpedoman's badge.

Jack appeared to like Ginger. Perhaps being friendly with his father helped things along, plus he had someone to talk to about Kenny. Jack never handed out free booze but he never once queried Gingers age or what he was doing in the pub. For that matter, neither did Yorkie Jack. Apparently he was a man and they treated him as one. All that despite having not long turned sixteen and looking all of twelve.

Ginger's mother didn't like him going in pubs and drinking beer. She never openly voiced her disapproval but she had other ways of making her feelings known; she had perfected a look that said it all. That look could stop an avalanche. That look had more impact than a lecture. She was not prepared to listen to any argument, however well thought out that argument may have been. That look said: 'I have my disapproving look on and I'm not ready to listen to anything you have to say. You might as well talk to a brick wall'.

She was of the old school where anything to do with waste was completely out of the question. Going in pubs and wasting money on beer was not even worth taking the time to discuss. That look was all the discussion needed. It said it all. In all fairness, she had just come through the austere times of the war where not only money was hard to come by but food as well. Although the war was well behind them, things had not improved a whole lot. There was still rationing on some food items and money wasn't all that plentiful.

She was a bit tunnel vision and there was only one point of view on anything she got a bee in her bonnet over. But she had a point and to know that her son had money in his pocket really didn't sit at all well with her. In fact Ginger knew that if he had turned over all his leave money to her, she would have accepted it as a matter of course. In the past some of the boys had mentioned, that when they arrived home with their housekeeping money their mother had let them keep it, but there was no such luck in Ginger's household. There was a little bit of paper, by way of a receipt, that had to be signed and returned to Ganges, to say that he had handed over three pounds and ten shillings and if he had not mentioned it within the first hour of being home, she would enquire as to where it – and the money – was!

Three pounds, a pound for each week of his leave, was what he was left with. It didn't seem a lot but it was probably on a par with his former school chums who were now working. Farm wages were a bit less than factory workers got in the city but with the addition of fares for the city workers it must have worked out about the same. Ginger didn't smoke, so that helped, but as the people of his age were away at work during the day he had to pal up with those a year or so younger and who were still at school. That meant that for his summer leave at least, which coincided with the school holidays, if he wanted a companion during the day he had to shoulder the expenses for two.

Highlight of the village's life was the weekly picture show in the village hall. Friday night was pictures night. It was a travelling one-reel projector outfit. As each reel came to an end the place remained in darkness until the next reel had been connected. The school kids sat in the front on about four rows of church pew type seats with the bulk of the audience sitting behind on individual chairs. That had been the set up for several years past and Ginger had always enjoyed his pictures. There was usually a serial and a main picture and sometimes a newsreel.

On his first leave Ginger had felt slightly out of place. Everything was exactly as he remembered it and those smells and noises came back to him as if he had never been away. Now, with a bit of time under his belt, he felt decidedly uncomfortable. He felt awkward and self-conscious. He continually had the feeling that he had outgrown the friends that he had known for years and never more so than in that makeshift cinema.

There were one or two that had always been troublemakers and they were still up to their usual antics, which made him feel embarrassed for them; others had found girlfriends to be with. Sitting there he felt that nothing had changed, but at the same time, everything had changed. He was sitting in the pews where he had sat for the majority of the past five years or so but he felt out of place. Before he had left for Ganges for that first time he had joined in the skylarking and had no doubt been as much of a nuisance as he felt they were being now. In fact he had been chucked out once for being a bit loud, but now he felt different. Somehow he felt aloof. It was as if he was hovering above them and observing from above. He felt as if all eyes in the place were on him and he was being associated with the noise and childish behaviour. That was Ganges discipline coming to the fore. Although they were only having a good time such behaviour would not have been tolerated at Ganges.

He wondered if he should remain sitting with the *children*, although some of them were as old as him and one or two others were older. He felt that by staying there he was being blamed for condoning their behaviour. He toyed with the idea of moving back to the individual chairs where the adults sat and distancing himself from them. But as they had paid a little bit extra for their seats he decided to stay where he was.

That picture show was the highlight of many peoples week. They came from miles around just to sit on those hard seats. They could have travelled to Norwich and gone to one of the purpose built cinemas but, of course, that entailed extra expense. There was the train fare to consider and the problem of getting home after. There was not always a train that late and even so, there was still the matter of getting home for those who lived miles from the local station. On top of that, the *proper* cinemas charged for the luxury of comfortable seats whereas the local makeshift picture hall only charged a shilling for the front benches and sixpence more for their best seats in the house.

Other than the local picture show a trip to Norwich was always considered an outing of significance. Although it was only about half an hour on the train village people didn't go to the city very often. Apart from those who worked in the city and were obliged to make the trip every day, people only made the journey two or maybe three times a year. Just prior to Christmas was always a must, if only to see the festive lights and the decorated shop windows. An outing was undertaken during the summer months, usually for the purpose of buying new clothes, particularly for the school children.

Being a small close-knit community everyone knew everyone and that meant that when someone bought a new coat or pair of shoes the whole place knew of the event, even down to whether the item was bought outright or on an instalment plan. Larger items such as a new bicycle or a television set, which were just becoming affordable for the richer working family, would be a topic of conversation for some time.

Ginger recalled his first pair of long trousers and how he had felt centre of attention being allowed out in them on Sunday morning. He felt that all eyes were on him and his new trousers and, no doubt they were. He never knew but it was almost certain that his mother would have held court, in the shopping queue or even in the street, about how smart her son looked on

Sunday in his new trousers. He recalled that it would be another year before he would be allowed to wear them all the time, every day.

Although his family had very little in the way of possessions, they were never without and nowhere near 'the poor of the parish'. His father always had work and they never went without a meal despite having nothing left over for what they considered luxuries, like things that some of the more affluent families had. But when he first joined Ganges he was surprised by the real poverty that some of the boys had come from. He found he wasn't anywhere as badly off as some. Even though the war was a fading memory, having been over for about eight years, some boys confided that they had never had pyjamas before, a few, mostly Londoners, had never had sheets on their bed and one or two had never even had a bed to themselves before.

Several of the new recruits had come to Ganges straight from other naval and military establishments and they too were happy to declare that they had never had it so good. Word of former inmates who had endured the likes of TS Arethusa, Greenwich, St. George, Barnardo's and Holbrook Hospital School, which was not far from Ganges, was that they were all places to get out of at the earliest opportunity. Boys joining from those places settled in right away.

By Ganges standards, at this stage in his new career, Ginger was pretty comfortable. He was first class and the bulk of his Ganges year was behind him. Nevertheless, compared to some of his army friends, Ganges boys had it tough. His army mates joined up, or were conscripted in most cases, and were treated far better than the Navy treated their recruits, who had all volunteered. The army boys did six weeks training and then were dispatched into various places around the world as trained soldiers. Even during that basic training they were allowed out of an evening and at weekends. Although the army life was no bed of roses, from what Ginger had gleaned, it appeared that their basic training was a lot like the Annexe episode but with night leave after four o'clock and weekends off.

In many respects Ganges was like a prison. An open prison maybe, but a prison just the same. Once inside that gate they would remain there for three months. That was not open to question. They served their time, fifteen hours a day, seven days a week and were ordered to bed at nine-thirty of an evening.

Ginger didn't enlighten his friends with those choice titbits, it would have been too embarrassing.

Another Ganges ritual that he kept to himself was the routine for everyone returning from leave. All boys were obliged to go straight from the main gate to the gymnasium, where they had to strip off completely naked and present themselves in front of a medical officer seated on a chair in the middle of the floor. This was to ensure that they were not smuggling in any form of livestock secreted about their body. That was not a very pleasant implied accusation and one that Ginger preferred to keep to himself.

SEVEN

There was not many occasions when Ginger could say that Ganges, or Ganges routines, worked in his favour.

There was the Queens Birthday Review (QBR) back in early June and that was a good example of things going right for him.

The QBR was the biggest parade of the Ganges year and everyone took part. The whole establishment marched, drilled and practiced for weeks in advance of the big day. Everyone, that is, except Ginger's recruitment. When he joined the Annexe the QBR rehearsals were already under way. The new boys didn't know anything about it until the actual day itself and then they were only required as spectators.

They had transferred from the Annexe a week or so before and without knowing anything about it, and without knowing that it was even taking place, Ginger missed the biggest parade of the year and all the ballyhoo that went with it during the preceding six weeks or so.

Similarly, when their yearlong course was over they would be drafted out of the place by the time that the parade came around again. So there was no point in getting involved in all those extra drills and ceremonies for that one either.

During their year they had got away with it, and without using any cunning whatsoever had dodged the biggest and most involved parade of the year, not once but soon to be twice. The first time it was early days and they had not been in the place long. Not long enough in fact to realise the value of a 'green coat'. On that occasion he had not needed one because Ganges, bless her cotton socks, had worked it all out for him.

Another occasion that he was thankful for but had no control over was his joining-up date. Ginger had joined, with his recruitment, on May 5.

Although he wasn't aware of it at the time, Ganges summer routine started on May 1. That meant that as well as banishing the winter blues, the boys also discarded those rotten wool sea jerseys. Those things felt like they were knitted out of wire and barbed wire at that. They were scratchy and downright uncomfortable.

He recalled how itchy and uncomfortable those blue suits were the first time they tried them on and, looking back now, he was grateful they didn't have those sea jerseys to contend with as well.

May 5 was a warm sunny day, as was the remainder of the month, and those sea jerseys were not missed in the least. Once again Ganges had smiled kindly toward him.

His May joining date was pot luck; he had no control over that. That was the date they sent him through the post. Before arriving at Ganges he had no knowledge of Navy routines and to him, at home at the time, one date was as good as another. He had no idea what winter routine, summer routine or any other kind of routine was for that matter. But as luck would have it, May was the beginning of summer routine at Ganges – and probably throughout the entire Navy as well, for all he knew – which meant, for his recruitment, his year's incarceration consisted of two summers and only one winter.

Yes, those Ganges Gods had given him all the breaks there were to give and had decreed him the shortest amount of time possible in those rotten sea jerseys.

Two summers was good. It was a lot better than having to endure two winters. The only drawback to summer routine was that it was also cricket season but that was a very minor complication and didn't complicate anything at all really. Given the choice between two winters or two summers and cricket, he would settle for the cricket every time even though he wasn't much of a cricket player. When he was in the Annexe he managed to get one game of cricket although, strictly speaking, he wasn't meant to have been there. There wasn't very much sport in the Annexe but just the same, they had to change into sports rig every afternoon. On the day of his cricket excursion he just happened to be in the right place at the right time and managed to get away with it. Chief Bumble, the Annexe instructor had been otherwise engaged and hadn't noticed his absence.

By the time they had joined Hawke Division the cricket season was well under way and the sports field resounded to the traditional 'leather upon willow' every afternoon. Ginger had played a bit of cricket back home but football was his game really. He wasn't cut out to be a very good batsman, plus that cricket ball was a bit on the hard side and it hurt. So, by the time their first leave came around and they had returned from it on September 8, cricket gear had been stowed away for another season and goalposts were being erected.

It wasn't long then before the evenings started to draw in and the wind began to bring a distinct chill up from the river and beyond that, the sea. The sun still shone but it had lost some of its heat and, as the season wore on Ginger was glad of the extra warmth of the sea jersey that he hated so much. Worn over the sports shirt with their long sleeves, sea jerseys were good for keeping the wind and cold out and not a bit uncomfortable. Being goalkeeper Ginger was allowed to wear one and not even Batchelor questioned him.

There was one occasion, on a very cold afternoon with a bit of snow on the ground and frost in the wind, when Ginger and the boys of 49 mess mustered outside in the colonnade prior to a football game. It was bitter cold and Ginger, being goalkeeper, wore his gloves. He was the only one in the squad wearing gloves and, naturally, Batchelor spotted it. The scowl deepened on his face as he strode the full length of the colonnade at a fast pace his eyes fixed on Ginger. The entire division were mustered and they all watched him in silence.

His route was a straight line from his starting point at the south end of the colonnade and would terminate in front of the 49 mess football team, who were at the other end and next to the swimming bath. Batchelor moved at a very fast pace and at the same time he was swinging his arms in exaggerated marching. He had hit the jackpot – he had caught someone wearing gloves. Suddenly, as he neared Ginger, his face changed and took on a mildly embarrassed look as he realised something. He tried to stop quickly and his feet skidded on the concrete, causing him to flail his arms about and almost fall over backwards. He came to a halt about six feet from Ginger, that stupid expression still on his face. He had made a mistake. He hadn't thought it through and now he was trying to make it look like he was joking. It didn't work. Everyone knew him too well.

With that half smile still on his face, he tried the friendly approach. It never worked with him, they all knew better, and on top of that he knew it.

'Are you goalkeeper this afternoon, Lambert?' he enquired in a false patronising way. The authoritative tone had gone. He had realised too late.

'That's correct sir,' Ginger replied, with an even sillier singsong voice that one would talk to a baby with, staring straight into the thin-ringer's face only a matter of feet from his. He was afraid of Batchelor, they all were, but Batchelor always seemed to single him out; he was fed up with always being Batchelors pet hate. There was absolutely nothing that he could do about it and he would just bring more trouble upon himself, and in all probability the rest of the mess as well, if he voiced his feelings by way of a complaint. The best he could retaliate with was that same silly patronising voice that Batchelor had used. It was certain that Batchelor knew that Ginger was mimicking him but there was not much he could do about it without revealing his own unnecessary interference.

The game had not been won yet and they all knew that the incident would not be forgotten. Batchelor could still pull him out of the team and give him some form of punishment to help him save face. But there were a lot of other people watching, including instructors.

'Well take those gloves off and carry them to the sports field,' he snapped before turning abruptly and marching back to where he had come from.

He had no reason to be there, except his personal ego. In his eagerness to show what a big man he was by browbeating someone - anyone - in front of the whole division, he had shot himself in the foot. It should have been in his head.

Batchelor was predictable. The good thing about him, if there was such a thing, was that he was always the same. The boys quickly learned how to take him and that was to treat him with suspicion and caution at all times. It didn't take long to figure him out, after all he almost told them what to expect from him. He never changed, or at least they never saw any change in him. His train of thought was a very narrow tunnel vision and always nasty. He was also reliable. He could be relied on to be nasty at any given moment, day or night. He was never any different in front of them. Whether the divisional instructors saw him in a different light was hard to tell. He showed them very little respect. How he behaved toward them in the divisional office, there was no way of telling. The instructors must have known what he was like; they had witnessed his performances on more than one occasion. There was no indication as to whether they had put him straight in private or not. After all he was only a jumped up petty officer and not long before had been the same as them.

Instructors would never openly criticise a fellow instructor, not even one from another division. That policy probably stemmed from 'the old pals act' that had grown in senior rates messes throughout the Navy over many years.

'He's one of us, whatever he's done,' seemed to have been an unwritten commandment among Ganges instructors.

There was no way that instructors could say that they didn't know bullying by fellow instructors went on but there were not many who would be prepared to say so, not even the more reasonable ones among them, for fear of repercussions and being ostracised by their messmates in the instructors messes.

Usually Leverett and Batchelor's nastiness was restricted to when they were alone with the boys. That way they could do and say anything they felt like because there was no one to see or overhear. Many such episodes were kept within the confines of the mess where a bit of overheard, muffled shouting from within a mess deck could easily be explained away if an occasion for an explanation should ever be called for.

By the same token, throwing a personal tantrum on the parade ground would usually pass unnoticed and therefore unreported, because every one of them did it at some stage or another.

Screaming forth at the top of their voice was nothing unusual on the parade ground. They all did it all the time. Even making a class double around the parade perimeter for an entire period would not look out of the ordinary. Any instructor having a bad day could take his frustrations out on his class and, if questioned, could explain it away as some form of punishment for not getting a particular drill right.

Within a few days of transferring from the Annexe to Hawke Division all new boys had Batchelor figured out. They knew that he would go out of his way to find any minor little thing that he could go into a screaming fit over. As time progressed and they achieved first class status, it made absolutely no difference as far as he was concerned. The only let up for them as time moved on, was that he had a continual supply of new recruits every few weeks, straight from the Annexe, to occupy his attention and that helped to keep him away from the older hands, to some degree.

He made no concession for 'time served'. It didn't matter to him if it was their first week in the division or the last before leaving for good. If there was something wrong with dress or bearing, or something else wrong caught his eye, he would be there to make sure it didn't go unnoticed or unrewarded.

He went out of his way to try to be everywhere and not miss anything. He would appear at odd moments for no particular reason and then stand and stare, looking for anything that he could involve himself with. Sometimes he would be seen half hidden at the corner of a building, watching a class double by or, sometimes he would be waiting outside the seamanship block to catch them sauntering down the steps outside at the end of a session. He always seemed to be there. He never appeared to take any time off. Maybe he had nowhere to go and no friends to visit. Maybe what acquaintances he did have didn't want him in their home. Occasionally, usually on a Friday afternoon, they would leave the seamanship block or the school block at the end of a period, to be met by Batchelor. That was usually a sign that Petty Officer Jury and Leverett had gone home for the weekend. It also signalled that they would have Batchelor's company all weekend and, more to the point, he would have them all to himself and no one to question him and his actions.

On such occasions they also realised that it meant they would have him on their backs for the entire weekend. Scrubbing out their section of the CMG on a Saturday morning was bad enough, even if they were left alone to get on with it. But with Batchelor's close attendance the entire operation would become a nightmare. With him in charge they knew the place would have to be done over at least twice. The first time would not be good enough plus he would want to oversee every stage. Just scrubbing the tiled floor would not satisfy him until he had witnessed every scrubber stroke or had ordered large swathes to be redone. He would also ensure that the work would not be completed, to his satisfaction, until the stroke of midday. They knew what to expect from him. He had done it to them before.

On previous occasions, when they had had him all to themselves, or was that the other way round, people from other divisions had began trooping in for dinner only to find the Hawke section still had their tables and benches piled up. That meant that Hawke residents would have to help to put them back in order before they could get their dinner.

It was strange how that situation only arose when Batchelor was on duty for the weekend and 49 mess were the scrubbing party. He'd had a down on 49 mess ever since they first arrived in Hawke Division. He always waited around until the very last minute to ensure they didn't try to finish early. Holding the entire division up and making them wait for their Saturday midday meal, didn't make them very popular. Then there were the buckets, scrubbers and cleaning materials to be stowed away before they could get their dinner. It only happened a few times and only with the combination of Batchelor and 49 mess and, on those occasions, by the time Hawke Division and, in particular 49 mess, got to eat their dinner, most of the other divisions had eaten up and had gone, which didn't make them popular with the galley staff either. Naturally, by that time Batchelor had vanished. He was quite happy to display his anger and venom at boys but he was not going to chance it with senior ships company staff who had the authority to report him.

Ganges was hard. Instructors would tell them that it had to be hard. That was the way it was. Ginger could see no reason why it should be as hard and impersonal as it was. There was talk that they had it a lot easier than their predecessors. But there was always talk about how everyone had it easier than how it was way back when. In all fairness they did have it a lot easier with the introduction of the Central Mess Galley (CMG). Only a year earlier the boys had to carry trays of food into their individual mess decks and contend with all the dishing out and washing up that went with it. There were tales, relayed down the years, of cold dinners and bullyboys grabbing larger portions and leaving the timid with next to nothing. So yes, they did have it easier than it had been, at least as far as meal times were concerned, but it was still far too strict and formal with a lot of unnecessary intimidation and downright bullying from certain instructors. It could have been a much friendlier place and the boys would have learned just as well and been far happier doing it.

On one particularly very cold afternoon Ginger, and a couple of the others, had been detailed off to work in the CMG with the cooks. Not that he was allowed anywhere near the cooking.

The whole class were on a week long workship. All classes had a week of workship during their year at Ganges. They did no classes or instruction of any kind but instead they did all odd jobs around the 102 acre site and, indeed, further afield if the situation warranted.

When they arrived it was early afternoon. They walked into the kitchen area a bit hesitantly not knowing what to expect or who to report to. Various cooks were doing things that cooks do and pans were clanking, either together or as they were banged down on the cooking range top.

It was the first time Ginger had been in that section, the section where the cooking was done. It was a modern place, having only been open for about a year and still looked brand new. It was partly hidden from view from the servery where the boys picked up the meals and served their tables, so it was all new territory to him.

The trio of interlopers in their sports rig appeared to go unnoticed, as they stood there, unsure of what they should do next. They had been ordered to report to the galley and they assumed that this is where they were meant to be. For a few minutes they stood there watching all the activity going on in front of them undecided whether they should join in or wait until they were noticed.

But before they had time to formulate their work plan, the chief in charge approached them.

'OK you lads, I've got work for you,' he said.

He was a short man with thinning fair hair. He didn't look or sound particularly aggressive. He looked friendly enough and his voice carried no hint of anger, false or otherwise, and that in itself made a refreshing change. He stood looking at them for a few seconds then, as if inspiration had come to him, he chopped the other two off with a sweep of his arm.

'You two, follow me,' he said, more or less over his shoulder, as he walked away.

Ginger watched the others walk away quickly to catch up with the chief who led them to a large sink that had a pile of cooking trays alongside. Ginger couldn't hear what was being said but the message was loud and clear. They had the dirty cooking pots; they had the hot soapy water; they had a couple of hours …. he breathed a sigh of relief, at the same time wondering what the chief had in mind for him.

His attention drifted for a moment as the chief rigged the pot washers up with long rubber aprons and when he looked back again the chief was nowhere to be seen.

After a while he returned and with a curt: 'This way lad,' he guided Ginger to a large mechanical iron contraption that turned out to be the bread slicing machine. After showing him how to work it, he said with an abrupt but not unfriendly, 'Got it?' and walked away without waiting for an answer.

It was a hand-operated machine, which meant that he could turn the handle at his own speed and stop any time he wanted to. It was easy and a lot better than having to scrub out cooking trays. The loaves of bread, about two feet long, were placed onto a tray on the machine and then, as the handle was turned, the bread was forced toward a cutting blade and was sliced, with the slices falling into a basket on the other side of the blade. All that was then required every two or three loaves, was just to stack the sliced bread into another basket, ready for teatime. All boys had two slices of bread and butter for tea each day.

He was in his element. It was freezing cold outside and he was in the galley and in the warm. Most of his messmates were outside in that biting wind wearing their shorts and a sports shirt. He was in the warm with very little to do and all the time in the world to do it.

As the bread passed the cutting blade it also brushed past a block of butter, which automatically spread some on each slice. Ginger noticed that every once in a while a slice would get an extra coating of butter. When he finished his task the chief let him go early. It was only about five minutes or so but it gave him enough time to secrete a couple of the liberally coated slices, butter side to butter side, under his sports shirt as he made a hasty exit.

Those two slices were carefully hidden in his locker out of sight of prying eyes. He knew that he was taking a big chance but hoped the anticipated result would be worth it. He then, innocently, made his way back to the CMG for his two teatime slices.

After tea it was back to more work. As it was winter time and dark and very cold outside, the evening work was confined to indoors wherever possible, but that didn't mean that it was easier.

His class, 61 class, was assigned the swimming bath. Leverett saw them to the door, which was only across the road from Hawke colonnade so it was no big deal for him and it meant that he had a free period. He was happy with his anticipated free time and the boys were happy to get shot of him for an hour or two.

Inside the changing room they were met by a PTI and Leverett had gone.
'Right then. Undressed and into a slip as quick as you can.'

They stood looking at each other no one making a move. This was not a swimming session and, in any case, they were workship party.

'Well, come on then, whatcha waiting for!'

This time they obediently got undressed and placed their blue suit on the changing room benches, before filing naked into the poolside and picking up a slip on the way. As usual, Ginger was busy weaving a few more threads toward his green coat and that ensured that he was the last to enter. It was not a swimming period; they were there for cleaning purposes. That PTI had tins of scouring paste and a bundle of rags waiting for them. He wanted the tiles on the inside of the pool cleaned.

Straight away, Sweaty Gillette, Dereham, Doug Raines and one or two more elbowed their way forward, they wanted the deep end. As they struggled and shoved their way forward, Ginger was doing the same – but in reverse. He was allowing himself to be left behind.

Soon all the milling and shoving was over. The 'eager beavers' got their own way, not that there was any opposition and were in the pool, scrubbing with their cleaning paste. A couple of others had been told to wipe down the supports of the diving boards and there was nothing left for Ginger to do. He tried to look disappointed although not too much in case the PTI found room for him in the pool. He didn't want all that muck and paste in his hair and eyes. He tried his best to keep out of the way but as he was doing nothing it was difficult.

Eventually the PTI cottoned on. 'Find a squeegee or a mop ....' he ordered, '.... and keep the walking surfaces clear.'

Ginger didn't know where the mops were kept, but on the right hand side of the pool there were steps leading down to a cellar. He investigated and found it was the boiler room used to heat the water in the pool and showers. It was lovely and warm and he decided to stay for a while. It was so warm that he lost track of time and when he emerged he found that the tiles cleaners had finished and were in the showers and that someone else had mopped up the walking spaces around the pool edges; the job that he was meant to have done. The pool cleaners had been so busy showing off with diving to the bottom that no one had noticed his absence and now it was time to get changed ready for supper.

After supper it was the turn of the messdeck to receive attention. Since the deck had been coated with brown asphalt a few months previously, the 'scrubbing out' had become much easier. Before, the wooden floorboards took the better part of two hours to scrub and dry off, with beds having to be humped over to one side and then back again. Now all that was required was for each individual to polish under his bed and the space alongside. With everyone doing his own little bit, the whole operation could be completed in less than an hour.

It was not until the following morning that Ginger remembered his slices of bread. He knew the longer they were in his locker the more chance there was of his being caught. He knew that Batchelor would sometimes look closely at someone's locker at random. They could tell by the way things had been slightly disturbed, that is unless he found something wrong and then the whole contents would be scooped out on the deck. There was no way of knowing which locker, or indeed which mess, would receive his attention. That meant that the longer that bread was left laying about the greater was the chance of it being discovered.

Ganges boys were never over fed and those couple of slices of bread were as good as a banquet, if he could find enough time and privacy to eat them at his leisure. He was hungry when he nicked them just prior to tea time and he had intended to eat them straight after but events had overtaken him and there had been very little time.

Sometimes one of them would receive a parcel from home. That usually meant a box of cakes or biscuits. Unfortunately there was not enough to share with around fifty others, who all expected to be included. Mail call was just before dinner. Daisy, their badge boy, would collect the mail for the mess and anyone getting a parcel chit would be very popular.

Hunger gave the boys a good memory and, straight after dinner when the lucky recipient collected his parcel from the mail room, which was alongside the mast, he would have a reception group waiting to escort him to his bedside and locker upon his return.

Ginger had received a few parcels from home during his first few months in the place, including one when he was in the Annexe and an ignorant Royal Marine 'postie' had smashed the box and crumbled most of the cakes. But after a while of enforced 'sharing' or having the goodies pilfered out of his ever-open locker, he told his mother not to send any more, as much as he appreciated them. He knew the same fate would befall his bread if the word got out. It would be: 'Gis that here' or 'I'll tell 'sir' that you stole it from the CMG' from the bully-boys. He couldn't understand why they never got beaten up or had their ribs kicked in, especially now that it was dark early. Everyone knew who they were. Everyone knew what they were like. Nobody liked them. Their survival probably was because they never went anywhere alone.

As it was so cold, coke braziers had been lit and placed in the outside toilet block, next to Hawke, to keep the pipes from freezing.

Straight after breakfast Ginger took his pilfered bread down to toast it on the brazier. As it was not clean clothes day there was plenty of time before Divisions. He had found an old bit of wire that he fashioned into a crude toasting fork and began preparing his snack all on his own and out of sight of everyone.

As the bread began to toast it smelled lovely and reminded him of home. He didn't think of home a lot but, for some reason the smell of toast brought back pleasant memories. A little bit of cheese in the sandwich would have been wonderful but he couldn't have everything. With one side of his bread done, he turned it over on his improvised toasting fork. The aroma filled the air, it smelled lovely.

Then suddenly: 'That boy there!'

It was bloody Batchelor.

'What do you think you are doing?'

It was obvious what he was doing but the best Ginger could muster was a feeble 'Er'.

'I asked you a question boy,' he thundered down through that awful Kraut nose. 'Where did you get that bread from?'

It made no difference where it had come from. He was caught and Batchelor would make the absolute most of it. With a bit of time to think Ginger could have said it had come from a parcel from home. It wouldn't have made much difference because there would have been a rule about heating food from home on naval property or eating outside of designated meal times or at least a dozen other reasons why Ginger was wrong and Batchelor had someone to browbeat.

'I, er, er umm,' was the best that Ginger could come up with. He was up against Batchelor and nothing he could say would make the slightest bit of difference.

Batchelor snatched the toasted bread from the improvised fork and threw it into the brazier, lifting his foot up and pushing the heel of his boot into it, pushing it down.

Ginger stood watching his toast being consumed by the red hot coals. So near and yet so far. He was really annoyed. Annoyed at losing his toast that he was looking forward to but more annoyed that Batchelor had deliberately burnt it just so he couldn't have it. He watched it disintegrate. It looked good. It smelled lovely.

'Why did you steal bread from the Dining Hall?' Batchelor demanded to know.

Ginger was livid. He toyed with the thought of punching or kicking the thin-ringer. Pushing his face into the red-hot coals also crossed his mind. He was shaking with anger but sense prevailed. He stood staring at Batchelor for a few seconds and then turned and walked away.

'Come back here. That boy. Report to me. Come back here!' Batchelor bellowed after him.

Ginger didn't even look back. He was out of it; he could take no more from the man. He strode quickly toward the divisional office. He intended to report Batchelor immaterial of the consequences. He hadn't thought if anyone would be there that early in the morning. Before he reached the office door it opened and Petty Officer Jury came out. He looked surprised.

'Lambert. What are you doing here?' he enquired

Ginger tried to walk past. Jury caught his arm. 'What's up. Where are you going?'

Ginger was trembling. He shook his arm free.

'I'm going to see the DO,' he said through gritted teeth.

There was no politeness, no respect, no standing to attention. He hadn't thought it through. What was he going to tell the DO? That he had been caught stealing? Batchelor had him so worked up that he couldn't think straight and now he was being rude to Cyril Jury, the only man in the place that had treated him decently.

Luckily, Jury persisted. With Leverett it would have been a different story.

'That bloody Batchelor.... I can't take any more of him.... I'll kill the bastard....' 'It all came out in a flood, most of it incoherent gobbledegook.

Jury listened until he had finished. Having got it off his chest, he felt calmer. The anger had left him. Suddenly he could see things in perspective again. He felt a bit sheepish. Jury didn't seem to notice, he was calm and collected. It was almost as if he was about to say: *feel better now?*

'Leave this with me. It's almost time for Divisions. Report back to your class,' he said, still blocking the way to the divisional office door.

Ginger was glad that he was blocking the door. He didn't want to see the DO any more. What would he say to him. He couldn't go through all that again. He would make himself look a right idiot. The DO would back Batchelor one hundred per cent; there was no question of that. Batchelor was nowhere to be seen.

Within a few minutes the call was sounded for Divisions. When they mustered Batchelor was there. Ginger tried not to look at him and Batchelor appeared to keep a lot of distance between them. He was not sure if that was a good sign or not. They were on workship so Batchelor could call him away any time he wanted to without disrupting any classes. But nothing happened. Just the same butterflies in his stomach changed from a soft shoe shuffle into a can-can as stand-easy approached.

They got a mug of milk and a sticky bun at stand-easy each day. Someone brought back the milk and buns from the galley and they all tucked in. Batchelor and Jury were nowhere to be seen.

After stand-easy most of them were dispatched to No. 3 gym. There was not much to do and it seemed that they had been sent there to keep them out of sight. It was a heaven sent opportunity for Batchelor to take them on, or at least to single Ginger out for his personal attention. Ginger was on tenterhooks but there was no sign of Batchelor.

A few of the boys swept the gym floor, although it didn't need sweeping and most of them just sat around talking. They couldn't go on the apparatus because they were wearing boots. They were left entirely alone, a most unusual situation. Luckily it was Leverett's day off otherwise he would have found them something to do. It had all the hallmarks of the lull before the storm.

But nothing happened. Every time Ginger saw Petty Officer Jury his heart skipped a beat but Jury never showed him any undue attention or by the same token, never ignored him either. He made a point of keeping clear of Batchelor as much as was possible.

The incident with the toast and the business outside the divisional office were never mentioned again. Ginger felt it prudent to let sleeping dogs lie.

EIGHT

The boys knew their year-long incarceration was nearing an end when they were issued with a hammock. They had already been measured up for their sea-suit so they had an inkling that their time was coming to a close. The sea-suit was a tailored suit that everyone was issued with just prior to his departure. Ginger's class mustered under the mast to be measured up by the shore based naval tailor and then a week or so later the new suits turned up – tailor made and tiddley jack. But hammocks were not required at Ganges and so were not issued until almost the last minute. Not that they needed any reminder of how close their leaving date was, that little topic was never very far from their mind as time marched on.

The hammock issue consisted of two canvas hammocks, a hammock mattress, two mattress covers, a blanket and a pillow. Everything then had to be stamped with the owners name with block capital letters about an inch square. Then Ganges being Ganges, as soon as the paint was dry all that extra stuff had to be sewn over with blue wool. Even at that stage of the game and with them being out of the place in a week or two, Ganges rules decreed that the names had to be sewn over. Ginger recalled their early days in the Annexe and how the instructor boys had to sew their names in their tropical kit, which had just been issued to them. Even though they had finished their course and had been selected to teach nozzers for a few weeks before going to sea, They were still Ganges boys and as such, their kit had to be sewn over with the dreaded red silk. It was Ganges tradition. Ginger's recruitment managed to avoid that delightful chore by not getting issued with any tropical kit.

But those mattress covers and blanket were there to be done. Unlike the remainder of their kit, which was sewn over with red silk in chain stitch, the hammock contents were done in an over and over stitch in blue wool. In the Annexe the sewing was quite possibly devised as a way of filling in time during their very first week. There seemed to be no other explanation. But why they persisted with the sewing at the other end of the year-long course was hard to understand. It was hard work and it was unnecessary work. Pushing a needle through the blanket wasn't any great hardship but those mattress covers were something else. They were constructed out of some kind of material akin to the stuff used to make mailbags and was a right cow to sew through. A sailmaker's palm would have made their lives a lot easier, especially as it was an unnecessary task in the first place. Once out of Ganges the sewing over of names was not required any longer.

But the end of the sewing didn't bring an end to the hammock episode. As soon as the needlework was completed they embarked upon the next stage of the hammock preparation – *pointing & grafting!*

Attached to the hammock, or very soon would be, were the ropes for hanging them up, or 'slinging' as hanging them up was called. At each end of the hammock were sixteen brass eyelets. Into these would eventually be sixteen pieces of thin line, known as nettles. These nettles, sixteen at each end of the hammock, culminated at a metal ring, about fifteen inches away. From the ring stretched a length of one-inch rope that would secure the hammock to its moorings, ready for the owner to sleep in. These lengths of rope were known as clews.

When not in use, the hammock would be lashed-up for stowing away during the day. The bedding would be wrapped up inside the hammock and lashed up with another length of rope, very aptly called the 'lashing'. A correctly lashed-up hammock would be secured with eight overhand knots along its length and the contents would be fully secure. Word was that a correctly lashed-up hammock would keep a man afloat for hours, should the occasion arise.

This then, was the story of the hammock, as told to them by Leverett and Batchelor. Leverett appeared to be in a particularly good mood as he relayed his version of the hammock saga to them. He told them how a former shipmate of his had put an eye splice in the end of each of the nettles, to make changing hammocks easier. He told them that each of the nettles was passed through one of the eyelets and then a length of rope, the same size as the lashing was threaded through all the eye splices in turn, thus making it simpler to pull out and release the hammock and saving all those individual knots to be untied and then retied again.

However welcome that little bit of light relief was, it didn't help much when they were introduced to pointing & grafting.

Pointing & grafting was a way of finishing off ropes to make them look attractive; a bit in the style of the fancy bell ropes that are sometimes seen in pubs and on naval establishment bells. It was Leverett who was the one to teach them the intricate craft that had to be done on each end of the two clews and the lashing. It was slow and somewhat tedious and it took hours to complete each one.

The grafting was done on the eye splice end of the clews and the lashing. One tuck only was made of the splice and then the ends were completely unravelled, dampened and made into small rats-tails. These were then woven in an under-and-over method to form the 'graft'. The pointing was very

94

similar except the bulk of the rope end was reduced in size as the point progressed, leaving the end to culminate in a point.

However tedious was the work, the finished job really looked the bees knees and every single one of them felt a sense of achievement. It was all their own work and they were proud of the result. At that stage they didn't know that it was all absolutely unnecessary; to them it was a job well done. Maybe it was another of little idiosyncrasies, those enterprises that were peculiar to Ganges. Ganges was full of them. But on the positive side it did introduce them to the basic art of the manufacture of tiddley bell ropes and other fancy work which some, if not all of them, could find useful as their naval career progressed.

As soon as the pointing & grafting was completed, the next stage in the hammock saga was to teach them how to 'lash up and stow', and that episode came under the tutelage of Batchelor. There were no eyebolts, hooks or hammock bars around so they were obliged to make use of the vertical struts that were holding up the roof of the colonnade outside the mess door. Batchelor had them all out in the colonnade. He was in his element. He had boys there under his control just the way he liked it to be.

He was still Batchelor and they still feared him but he seemed to have mellowed. His face was still hard and set into his customary scowl and his body language suggested that he wasn't there out of kindness. Nevertheless the atmosphere was a lot lighter than it usually was when he was around. None of them felt brave enough to push their new found freedom to see how far his lenient mood would stretch however. They stood in silence as he expounded the technique for lashing up a hammock correctly. Picking on someone's hammock, the first one to come to hand, he tied it to two adjoining struts and commenced with the routine, explaining every stage as he went. He appeared to be a different person as he carefully explained each manoeuvre, even reverting back to go over a particular small point again, as the occasion arose.

When he had finished and everyone was satisfied that they knew how to lash-up, it was their turn to put their newly learned theory into practice. The lashing-up process took a long time to get through, with only a few at a time being able to use the limited struts of the colonnade but Batchelor's patience was remarkably serene. He stood quietly by watching but, most unlike him, he didn't interfere unless somebody got into a bit of a muddle. Then he would step forward with a curt: 'Not like that, boy, haven't you been paying attention?' Naturally, at that everybody within range had to gather round while he explained and demonstrated once again: a complete contrast to the

Batchelor of old. Each of the 49 mess occupants turned up with what looked like a bundle of old rags and, thanks to him, each boy went away with a correctly lashed up hammock.

When it was Ginger's turn he was apprehensive but Batchelor gave no outward sign, either by word or action, of their earlier debacles and he went away, somewhat surprised and more than a little confused but with his hammock correctly lashed up just like everyone else.

Batchelor played a blinder that day and, although the boys didn't realise it, or maybe they were reluctant to acknowledge it, they owed him a vote of thanks. He taught them how to sling their hammock correctly; he taught them how to lash up a hammock correctly; he taught them in a kind and considerate manner and he taught them well. They had been told once and they had absorbed the knowledge from that one lesson on that one-day. That knowledge would have to hold them in good stead when they got to sea, because there would be no-one to help them then, and how they slung their hammock unaided would be how they would have to sleep in it, he told them.

Continually stroking the unravelled strands of rope into small sections, coupled with pulling them tight at each tuck on the pointing & grafting made their fingers sore with some of them even acquiring blisters, so they were glad to get outside and onto the parade ground occasionally. Although parade drill had not come easy to the majority of them in the beginning, it made a welcome break for sore fingers and it got them out into the sunlight.

They had done so much parade drill and rifle drill over the past year that when it came to their passing out examination they absolutely waltzed it away. It made a pleasant change from sore fingers getting worse and tender from the rope strands of their hammock lashings and, on the other hand, sitting in the mess with a ropes end made a break from the parade manoeuvres of their final passing out. In some obscure way the two contrasting sessions complimented each other.

POGI Jury had brought them on slowly over the previous months and, although they were aware that they had become pretty good, they were proud to note just how good they had become when it really mattered. With Cyril Jury having shown them every step of the way, culminating in their final test under the eagle eye of an examining officer, where they had the parade ground all to themselves, they never put a foot wrong.

Ginger was in his element. He had never found that side of things very difficult. He had had a comparatively easy ride with parade drill all through the previous year. He'd had a bit of a head start over most of them from the very beginning and he didn't really mind that kind of instruction. It was easier than most of the other stuff that they had to contend with. From those very early days he had felt comfortable with marching and then later, rifle drill and he couldn't ever recall being singled out. Naturally he progressed as time progressed, they all did. Now, at this end of their course, every one of them had it weighed off to a fine art.

There was satisfaction to be gained from hearing that one crisp *shunt* as feet came together as one when being called to attention or to a halt. A different story from their earlier attempts when that 'shunt' sounded more like the clatter of a machine gun as individual feet did their own thing and mostly in their own time.

Ginger enjoyed the parade ground, although *enjoyed* was maybe a bit strong. He didn't like the Divisions that they had to attend every Sunday morning; all that standing about and the individual scrutiny that went with it was a bit awesome; and the 'Shotley Shuffle' of Shotley Routine fame was not to be recommended. But in the main, parade drill and rifle drill was a doddle. It was comfortable and he felt comfortable when he was engaged in it, just marching up and down.

Any idiot could march up and down and most, if not all, parade ground activity was geared towards a squad rather than the one-to-one of other lessons. Which meant that unless you did something drastically wrong you would never get noticed and singled out, unlike in a classroom or confined to a whaler or cutter on the river, where the instructors eye would be on you all the time. Ginger also helped his cause with a self preservation card, that he had figured out for himself, and that was simply: *lose yourself in the middle of the centre rank and keep in time with everyone around you and you can't go wrong!*

That philosophy had kept him out of trouble for a year and it was still paying dividends, although it was doubtful if he needed that extra protection any longer. Even in those early days in the Annexe and for the first few weeks in the main establishment, he felt that he was ahead of most of his classmates and it amused him to see how some of them struggled with even the most basic of manoeuvres. In those early days he really hated the place and wished over and over that he hadn't joined up. It was much harder than it needed to be. The only military training he had done was a once a week session with the army cadets; that was where he had learned his basic drill. Even learning from scratch was easier than learning the Ganges way. But nevertheless he had learned the basic lessons and that gave him enough time to marvel at the antics of most of his messmates.

With Daisy, their Badge Boy, out in front and carrying a sword, they marched up and down in their blue suit with white belt and gaiters, changing direction, forming squad, forming two ranks from three and back again and every other conceivable drill in the text book, they just could not be faulted.

The parade test started of with Petty Officer Jury taking them through a succession of warm-up routines, under orders from the examining officer, before moving on to the more advanced stuff of forming squad, changing direction, counter marching and other weird and wonderful contortions.

Every one of them was on top form. They all knew it. They knew there had not been a single mistake. The examining officer knew it as well although he gave no indication. But most of all POGI Jury knew it. His face beamed with delight as the realisation hit him that they were doing their utmost for him. Cyril Jury was delighted with them and their performance and it showed in his normally deadpan face. His strictly 'Navy through-and-through' attitude went by the board; he struggled to keep his emotions under control. *His boys* had come through for him; they had not let him down. They had done what he knew they could do.

Petty Officer Jury had never had an axe to grind or an ego to feed. He was a genuine sort of chap; his emotions, when he couldn't help but let them show, were for real. The boys were as pleased for him as he was for them. To see him that happy made the whole thing worthwhile.

Jury had arranged for the establishment photographer to take pictures of them during their final parade test and the photographer, Reg Fisk, snapped away happily as they marched up and down. At the conclusion of the examination PO Jury marched them round to the rear of Nelson Hall, the drill shed, and onto the grass of the playing field where he had them in different poses: at the slope, at the present, and at the order, with him standing at the rear of them saluting proudly and wallowing in his moment, while photographer Mr Fisk did the business from all manner of angles.

Cyril Jury was absolutely delighted and they were pleased that they had not let him down. The man was a perfectionist and he just naturally assumed that everyone else would want to be as well. He had brought them on slowly until they had reached the peak of their training and he had achieved it all without the customary screaming, shouting and bullying.

He always stood to attention in front of them when he addressed them and now it was all over he did so again. He was absolutely delighted, they could tell although his naval training would never allow him to show it. He tried his best to congratulate them but the words didn't come easily. The man was close to tears and was beside himself with emotion. It was gratifying to know that he felt so highly of them but, at the same time, it was slightly embarrassing to see him like that.

Finally he said: 'You have done me proud. You have done yourselves proud, each and every one of you. Thank you all.' Then turning to Daisy, the badge boy, he continued: 'Right then Daisy, march them away, return rifles and dismiss please.'

On that particular occasion he even said *please* because he was so proud of them. That was a word unknown to Ganges instructors. That one little word meant a lot to them; it got their attention and impressed itself upon them. It showed that he really meant what he said. He was the sort of man that would never have been so open unless he was sincere. Ginger remembered the last time he had seen Cyril Jury in a similar emotional state. That was the time they had been caught skiving gym class. That time he was lost for words too. Although he was emotional on that day, it was not through anger but from disappointment. He was sad, disappointed and possibly a little embarrassed on that unforgettable day. This time it was a far more enjoyable occasion.

With the parade exam behind them they were well into their finals. Where that word had come from was a bit of a mystery. No one in authority had used the term, it seemed to have slipped into their vocabulary unnoticed, probably overheard from more senior classes as they undertook their finals. Whether the phrase was finals, final examinations, passing out or whatever it was they were lumbered. They were well and truly on the treadmill and there was no getting off until every possible scrutiny of them had been completed.

True to the Ganges tradition they had never been told that they were now on their final tests – their finals. So they were never sure when those tests actually started. They had done their parade ground drill bit and had passed with flying colours but was that the first test they wondered, or had they started earlier. Ganges boys were assessed – or tested – all the time, it was an ongoing thing. There was no way on earth that they would have progressed to the end of their year-long course if they had faltered anywhere along the way. They would have been back-classed into a class that was six weeks later in starting and obliged to go over that last six weeks training all over again. No one from 49 mess suffered that indignity although a couple of people were back-classed into them in their later stages, although it was true to say that both of the new boys had not been able to take their finals with their previous class due to illness.

It seemed to Ginger that the final examinations Ganges inflicted upon everyone were really just a going-through-the-motions exercise because they were assessed every step of the way throughout their training. If any were unable to keep up they would have been back-classed and back-classed yet again if necessary. Which meant that by the time they reached the end of their course the powers-that-be knew that every boy was ready and able to pass the final tests – thereby making the actual tests unnecessary.

Although they could perform any task set before them, or at least that's what their two class instructors had led them to believe, the biggest fiasco was the signals test. One morning they were marched to the seamanship block for morse (sound and light) semaphore and boatswains call piping tests.

For reasons best known only to himself, Petty Officer Leverett had already enlightened them with the good news: 'Don't worry about the morse code, they won't be testing you on that.'

That was music to Ginger's ears. His morse code was absolutely non-existent, it most definitely wasn't one of his strong suits. Not that he had any strong suits to boast of in the first place. He had put himself out just far enough to make a spot for himself in the middle of the pecking order, just far enough down so as not to attract attention and not that far down to receive the wrong kind of attention. He fitted comfortably into the middle order. However, he would gladly have swapped someone's parade session for his W/T exam. They had had very little training on signals at any time, so maybe it was known that they wouldn't be expected to perform in those disciplines.

The boatswains call test was the first test to be carried out. It was performed in front of a thin-ringer that they had never seen before and Ginger blew, trilled and warbled his way through the entire repertoire …. to a conclusive fail mark.

The boatswains call challenge carried two grades of pass mark, in addition to the fail category that Ginger had managed to attain.

Those among them who had studied hard were rewarded with the presentation of a boatswain's call and chain as a first class pass – the chain to be worn around the neck instead of a lanyard, by way of a status symbol. All the calls and how to execute them were displayed in their seamanship manual in the form of a graph. Each call was designated so many seconds and, for the purposes of the test, were measured with a stopwatch. Anyone almost up to standard but who had lost an odd second here or there, was given a boatswain's call but no chain, more or less as a runner-up consolation.

Some of their number trilled almost to perfection and proudly received their call. A select few others got it exactly right and won their chains as well. That select band included Ray Leeward and Shilling both of whom went on to compete in the Silver Call Competition where they piped their way to first and second places against all comers. The proud owners of the call and chain were allowed to wear their chain in place of a lanyard at every occasion when a best suit was called for.

Again someone, somewhere, let the cat out of the bag when, just before the semaphore test the word went round that they would be asked their name and have to spell it out with hand flags. This, again, was of great interest to Ginger because his knowledge of flag messaging was not quite up to the standard of his boatswain's call capabilities. Somehow he had learned a couple of rude words that he would send to anyone that was idiot enough to read them in the signal mess next door. They appeared easy enough to learn but that was the extent of his semaphore, everything else almost had him tying his arms into a knot.

However. he did find his name easy to learn:

L was simply the right arm in position one (for A) and the other diagonally opposite;

A simply meant dropping the left arm altogether;

M was putting the left arm back, one space down from where it was for L;

B was dropping the left arm again and raising the right one space;

E was the first position with the left arm, just over at one o'clock;

R was both arms straight across in a crucifix and that only left T;

T was bit tricky but it was only one position to learn and remember and that was *LAMBERT* off to a tee.

In front of that thin-ringer once again, surprise, surprise, he got it right. Breathing a sigh of relief as he waltzed out of the door he thanked his lucky stars that he wasn't asked what the chap behind him was called; he had no idea how to wave out his name – or anyone else's for that matter.

As the last of them came down the steps of the seamanship block, glum faced or happy as the case may be, to join the remainder of the class waiting outside, it brought to a close yet another segment of their *finals,* although it was not the last they were to see of the seamanship block. They still had ropes and splices; bends and hitches; buoys by day and buoys by night and a multitude of other *seamanlike evolutions* to contend with. But apparently that could wait. It was dinner time and, after dinner, they had the gymnasium and the PT examinations.

Physical training, or gymnasium work in general, was something else that Ginger took in his stride. He was slightly built so he didn't have a lot of extra weight to hump around. Slightly built but wiry and possibly a little stronger than his appearance might suggest. He had never been in a gym before joining Ganges and for the first couple of sessions he was completely out of his depth. He didn't even know the names of the various pieces of apparatus but, as time progressed, he learned and in a short space of time he was on a par with those that had done it before.

Mostly, gym work was enjoyable. They were there to learn and although it was physically demanding he found it interesting. Once in a while an odd PTI would feel the need to flex his muscles over some misdemeanour and the boys were obliged to let him have his moment of power by hanging from the wall bars until their arms could take no more, or doing unnecessary press-ups or strength sapping leg raises, but those moments apart, Ginger enjoyed being in the gym and, he suspected that the majority of the others did as well.

Somehow he felt free. It was lovely to wear just a pair of shorts, a sports shirt and plimsoles; it made a pleasant change from serge suits and heavy hobnailed boots. Over all the PTIs were not too bad. They had volunteered for the PT branch so they were happy in that kind of environment and they were geared to teach, to teach their favourite subject. Most times the boys had their own PTI for gym sessions. Each division had their own attached to the division. The Hawke man they had christened 'Mighty Mouse' almost from their first meeting, due to his stature. He was an agreeable enough chap, probably newly qualified and still keen to pass his expertise on to them.

Through him and his teachings, they were well up to standard and even ahead of it on occasion. Once in a while, toward the latter part of their year, they had had a *'fun session'*. That was simply a complete session doing things just for the fun of doing it. The reason being that they progressed so fast that they were outpacing the course curriculum, which meant that they had to waste a few sessions just so as not to get too far ahead.

Fun sessions were, as the name might imply, a lot of fun. They were still serious business and the boys were still doing gym work. But rather than course work that they were already up to the required standard with, they had a fun session where they would race around a circuit against each other, or in teams of four or five, or try to outdo each other with spectacular vaults over the box or racing up the ropes suspended from the ceiling and other like activities that anyone could come up with.

Although there was usually a certain amount of noise from the goings-on in the gym, they had to try to remain as normal as possible during those periods so as not to attract the attention of the chief-in-charge. Mighty Mouse was as pleased as they were to get a bit of variety into their drills and add a bit of colour and spice to the sessions, and some antics that he taught them he had brought with him from his last posting, which was in all probability the PT School.

But it had not always been like that. For their first few periods they had taken on the appearance of a gaggle of geese and most of them with broken wings, as they flopped and dropped all over the place. Mick Southern was one of the most uncoordinated people you could possibly meet, and Mac, a blond boy from London was not much better. Come to that, neither was Ginger. Although Ginger soon got the hang of things and quickly became up to speed, not particularly through determination but because he was interested, and he was beginning to enjoy himself away from the hustle and bustle and intimidation of everyday life outside the gymnasium walls.

One chap however, was never going to get it right, or even improve very much for that matter and that was Sim. Compared to Sim, Mick Southern and Mac looked like ballerinas. He really was that bad. Sim was tall and remarkably thin. With his long beaky nose, his thin arms and legs and his sticking out Adams Apple he looked like the stereotype caricature of a St. Trinians schoolgirl and was about as disciplined with his body. His arms and legs and indeed other parts of his body appeared to have individual minds of their own and flapped about like pieces of cotton in the breeze.

Sim was, to some degree, a bit of a loner. He was friendly enough and would speak to his immediate neighbours in the mess, if anyone took the trouble to talk to him. He had an uncanny knack for voices and could mimic certain people precisely. One of the other instructors in Hawke spoke in a breathless manner as if he had to force words out, particularly when giving loud orders; he became Sim's favourite party piece.

Sim would come into the mess gasping 'lef' right, lef' right, lef' right,' exactly the same as that instructor. He did it in front of Leverett one evening and even Leverett's permanently turned down mouth was forced to soften into a smile. Unfortunately Sims mimicry wasn't enough to save him and one day when they trooped back to the mess there was an empty bed and Sim had gone.

Their final examination in the gym was a piece of cake; a veritable walk in the park. There must have been some substance in the old saying: *train hard - fight easy,* because, however unwittingly, that was exactly what they had accomplished. In their case it was a variation on that theme – train hard and test easy – and that was precisely what they had done.

The PT Officer was the examining officer and Mighty Mouse put them through their paces, under the watchful eye of that PT Officer. A bit reminiscent of Cyril Jury and their parade drill episode, and just like Petty Officer Jury, Mighty Mouse knew what they were capable of and he laid it on. He was determined that they should score well and to that end he put them through all of the tougher routines. They knew what he was doing and why he was doing it and they responded well.

The floor exercises; the wall bars; the beam; the parallel bars; the ropes and the box, they flew through them all as if they were on wings, never putting a foot wrong. That was their second big obstacle passed and passed big time. They knew it, Mighty Mouse knew it, and the PT Officer knew it.

Pretty soon PO Jury knew it as well. Again he was delighted although this time he remained more in control of his emotions. He was pleased that they had done so well and he told them as much. But this time he hadn't taught them. It was doubtful if he could ever top the feelings that he had felt on their parade drill passing out day but just the same, he was their instructor and he was proud of them.

NINE

They felt good. They were well on their way. The final examinations – that had somehow acquired the all-encompassing, if somewhat obvious name of *finals* and had brought nothing but gloom and despondency down upon them – wasn't too bad after all now that they were into their stride and under way. To some extent the boys of 49 mess had surprised themselves.

Prior to participating in those final examinations, or at least before they realised that they had actually started on the finals merry-go-round, they had experienced a dark cloud of trepidation creeping up on them and that feeling got stronger and a lot more intense as it dawned on them that their time had come. Each of them felt it, it was the fear of being forced into the unknown. It was the Ganges way. They had had it drummed into them so much and so many times that their best was not good enough. Every one of them was convinced they were doomed to failure.

Both of their instructors, PO Jury and PO Leverett, had told them so often that their efforts could do with an extra polish that the boys were sure they were never going to be up to the exacting standards that Ganges demanded. However, it all came good when it was their turn under the microscope. They had no choice but to go for it and try their best and that is what they did.

The parade drill in particular appeared to be a great success. Possibly because Ginger found it comparatively simple, he could tell almost as soon as they did the inaugural march on that they were onto a winner. Like most of the others he had stomped his way through the learning curve that had brought them to the stage where they now were without really noticing if they were doing well or not and, in all honesty, not really caring or paying that much attention. But something, some indefinable something, told him on that day that they had come together as one unit. Maybe they had gelled before then and he hadn't noticed but on the day of their big test he couldn't help but notice. They were perfection and he secretly felt quite proud.

The final gymnasium test was good as well. Better than good. Once again they had performed as one man when the occasion demanded, and on the individual disciplines they never put a foot wrong either. Most of them liked being in the gym. The work was tough and they were there to learn but they were out of the limelight and away from the prying eyes that Ganges seemed to have cornered the market with, plus their PTI, Mighty Mouse, wanted to teach and he wanted them to learn. Maybe he was being assessed himself. Maybe all instructors were assessed. Who could tell?

Now that they had the parade drill and the gymnasium test behind them, the boys' confidence grew and, maybe, they even took on a slight swagger. Although they hadn't been told what the results of the finals they had taken so far were, they didn't need to be told; they knew they had done very well. Jury gave the game away with his 'I'm proud of you' speech and although Mighty Mouse hadn't actually said so, they knew that the gym test had also gone well. He wasn't an aggressive man but if they had messed up he would have told them after the examining officer had left. In any case they knew everything had clicked into place. They could feel it. They were on a high; they were on a roll. Suddenly they got into the spirit of things; they wanted to do well with everything.

The seamanship test was the one that most of them were dubious of. The signals, both morse and semaphore, were originally the ones to worry about but that turned out to be a non-event after they were told there would be no test for morse, and semaphore required that they learn just the letters to spell their own name. The seamanship fear was quite probably brought about by Leverett's involvement. They all had a cautious fear of that man ever since their first meeting and lessons with him were always an occasion to be on tenterhooks. They knew their seamanship but could they recite it correctly whilst under pressure and with Leverett hovering in the background?

Leverett had that effect on them. There was no question that he knew his subject but his method of teaching was through fear. Fear of getting something wrong coupled with the fear of incurring his wrath and having not only oneself but also everyone else on some late night punishment detail, ensured they kept on their toes at all times whilst in his presence. Leverett was not the type to concede that someone may genuinely be having trouble with something a bit complicated. His attitude was along the lines of 'if-I-can-do-it-so-can-you'. The fact that he'd had several years 'doing-it' and they had started off as green nozzers less than a year earlier, never entered his head. Or if it did, he made no concession.

He was a hard taskmaster but, as they say, *'the proof of the pudding is in the eating'*. Now, faced with the seamanship examination, it was time to taste the pudding.

The seamanship room was inside the seamanship block. A different thin-ringer was waiting for them as they trooped in apprehensively and stood quietly at one end of the room.

'Right then,' he started. 'Half of you on the line.' With that he chopped about half of them off with his arm and herded them toward a wire that had been stretched taut across the room. Short lengths of small diameter rope lay nearby.

Armed with a length of rope each they began tying knots and hitches to the wire, as he sang out what knot he wanted to see next. That session went well and the man seemed satisfied. It was matter of fact and he handled it as such. No emotion; no shouting; no bullying or browbeating. At the same time no friendliness. Just businesslike.

The second half completed their tasks on the wire then everyone was shepherded over to the ship model which stood on a table top in the centre of the room. There was not enough time for every one of them to go through an entire routine and, in any case, when the first one had completed whatever manoeuvre was called for, it would have been simplicity itself for the remainder to follow suit. So someone near the front was pressed into service.

'Right then,' sang out the examining thin-ringer. 'Stand by to drop anchor.' At that the 'appointed one' did preliminary checks in readiness for dropping the anchor. Everything just as they had learned and how Leverett had taught them. Every once in a while the man would stop proceedings and single out someone. 'Was that correct?' or, 'What did he do wrong/forget?' In each case the answer was that nothing was wrong or forgotten and the drill would continue. It seemed that thin-ringer was trying to catch them out by leading them to infer that something was not quite right but the boys were having none of it. They had gone over it enough times to know when everything was as it should be.

After that they moved on to a thing that looked like a little open boat. It was just a platform with a ships wheel on it and a gyrocompass attached to the front. It chugged round in response to wheel movements. Again there was not enough time for all of them to have a go and about half a dozen got to perform course changes and other ship's wheel manoeuvres under the officer's instructions, while the rest watched and were quizzed on proceedings.

They saw seamanship in a different light, courtesy of that man. Although he was testing them – and presumably looking to find fault – the session was interesting. Leverett had been hovering in the background all the time but had not said a word and they had all but forgotten about him. They had got themselves involved. They had got so carried away that they had forgotten it was a test; they were surprised at just how much they actually knew. As with the parade and gymnasium before, they had absolutely waltzed through. Nevertheless it was a test and they had to be on top form all the time. They now saw that if they could have removed Leverett and his ever-present threat of fear from the equation, seamanship was interesting.

So it went on, day after day, test after test. The merry-go-round kept merrily going round. But the boys were more than equal to the challenge. Learning had been drummed into them all day every day, ever since those early days when they first arrived from the Annexe. Indeed even before that because, although they had other things to occupy their minds in those days, their training had started, in effect, from day one. Naturally they didn't realise that fact but everything was geared toward their learning process. Simple things that they took for granted like Divisions, meal breaks, stand-easys and even the washhouse helped them to adapt; they were being accustomed to service routine every step of the way.

The learning had crept up upon them and, albeit subconsciously, they had absorbed that knowledge. They were surprised by how much they actually knew. Many, many things were learned and most were instantly filed away in the back of their brain somewhere. Now, when any of them was asked a specific question, they could instantly come back with a specific answer.

There were several more, what Ginger had christened 'odd-bods and bits' tests. Some were focused on as major events and took up a complete session while others, although apparently important, such as gunnery tangents, elevations and aircraft recognition plus shooting operations, were slotted in where ever an opening occurred. The same was applied to buoys; there were a lot of different buoys; lots of different shapes and lots of different colours. Then there were also the lights on buoys at night to contend with. Each buoy had its own distinctive series of flashes, each different and each to be learned and tested on.

Somehow the boys of Hawke 49 mess had surpassed themselves. They had exceeded their own expectations by far. When it came right down to it, they had come through with flying colours. Apart from a final kit inspection, which was a formality and just an excuse to have the captain involve himself in their last days under his control, their finals were over and they had done remarkably well.

The kit inspection was the last thing on the final examinations agenda and when it came around they knew their ordeal was over. Pass or fail, sink or swim, whatever the outcome of the results they were given, that was it. When they laid out their kit for the last time the remainder of the results were already known to everyone except them. Whatever they had achieved or not achieved for that matter, stood as their testimony. It was over. Almost as soon as they started out they realised that they were up there among the best. They hadn't noticed with the day-to-day activities but when it really mattered, it showed. They were good and what's more they knew it. But, having cottoned on to the fact that they were good, had they become complacent? Had they been lulled into a sense of over confidence? Had they become too cocky?

Those questions and more were answered after the kit inspection was completed.

They were obliged to transport their kit down the Covered Way to an old empty building that none of them could remember ever seeing before. It was completely empty with bare walls and a wood block floor. Maybe the idea was to have a space without encumbrances to distract from the immaculately laid-out kit or, more likely, it was to make it easier for the Captain to carry out his inspection without having to negotiate his way into different messdecks every few days, as other classes did the same with their kit.

The kit fiasco was a formality. They had endured a kit inspection every other week for the past year, plus a few extras that Leverett had kindly bestowed upon them for any minor misdemeanour, real or imaginary, that he could come up with. So they knew what was expected of them where that was concerned and, of course, Leverett had scrutinised every single article long before the appointed inspection time. Batchelor, too, had shown a very keen interest. That man just couldn't help himself – he had to be involved. Their unofficial inspection was far more demanding and thorough than that of the inspecting officer – the Captain, who hardly looked. His contribution was just to smile continually, nod occasionally, and mumble 'well done' to someone here and there, as he circumnavigated his way round and out the door once more.

Naturally, every segment of their passing-out tests carried an element of suspense if not to say fear with it. Fear of failure or of not being quite up to scratch, or fear of incurring the wrath of Leverett or Batchelor. But those fears and uncertainties, real as they were, subsided a touch with each passing test, as they knew things had gone well for them.

But straight after the kit inspection – their 'final final', all remaining doubts disappeared when Petty Officer Jury told them that the Captain had asked to have his congratulations on a splendid turn out relayed to them. That was an accolade they never expected to hear. That was the icing on the cake. They had passed with flying colours. Although the results were still unofficial, they all knew it, every one of them, and that earlier swagger could now be justified. They had conquered Ganges passing-out examinations and done so with ease. It didn't feel easy at the time but looking back they had breezed along. No sweat. They were top dogs.

The following morning Petty Officer Jury came into the mess as usual, just prior to the Tannoy bursting into life with the call for Divisions. He seemed in no hurry to do anything or talk to anybody. Then as the Tannoy clicked on with its familiar buzz he managed to put himself in a position with his back to the double doors that led to the passage and down the stairs, effectively barring their way out.

They were all dressed and ready for Daily Divisions and the day ahead and as they started to file forward to comply with the bugle call that was now in full swing Jury held his hand up for silence, getting ready to speak for the first time.

His usual opening gambit was: 'Well, come on. You heard it, whatcha waiting for.' That was nearly always the same and often accompanied by the clanking of a stick around the inside of the dustbin to lend effect. But this time it was different. They stayed where they were, waiting for him. This had never happened before. Everyone else would be down below by now and none of them had even left the mess yet.

Then, as the last strains of the bugle call and the quartermaster's voice died away, Jury spoke. 'Just hold it where you are.' His face betrayed no emotion but his voice was softer, almost friendly. There was none of that 'Whatcha waiting for' aggressiveness about him. Shades of their Shotley Routine days came flooding back although then there was plenty of aggression.

But there was no hint of anger, either by word or action. His tone was still soft. He stood where he had been from the start, just inside the door. Only his head moved. Was it imagination or was he deliberately looking at each of them in turn. After what seemed like a long time, with him catching and holding everyone's eye, he cleared his throat.

'I have the results of your finals here,' he said, producing some papers from inside his jacket. His face still gave no clue although his voice appeared to have taken on a more formal and slightly disapproving tone. It looked as though they hadn't done as well as they thought they had after all.

He looked around the assembled faces again but couldn't keep up the charade any longer. His usual non-descript face broke into a broad grin, his entire face beamed with delight.

'You have excelled yourselves. These results are absolutely splendid. You have done yourselves proud. You have done everybody proud.' He told them. He looked down as if to read the papers to give himself a second or two to control his emotions, before continuing. 'Each and every one of you. As individuals and when you have been called upon to perform as a unit. Thank you all. I am proud of you. Thank you again.'

110

Cyril Jury always stood to attention when addressing them but on that occasion they saw the real man. This was not Ganges, this was personal. For once, his Navy-through-and-through went out of the window. He was having trouble controlling his jubilations. They'd seen him display his emotions a couple of times before: once when they blotted their copybook by getting themselves on Shotley Routine and more recently, straight after their parade drill test. But this time it was something else. He was close to tears. Tears of joy. Maybe tears of gratitude. He was boiling over with emotion and now that they were alone, his feeling got the better of him.

The boys stood not knowing quite how to handle the situation. They were pleased to learn that they had done well but mostly their happiness was for Cyril Jury. They were pleased that he was pleased. They hadn't started out with any specific plans to do well, or not to do well for that matter. It was just Ganges putting them under the microscope yet again; another milestone to be reached and they had reached it. Cyril Jury was delighted with them and he couldn't stop telling them so. His enthusiasm was contagious; he had infected them all. Ginger just hoped that he wouldn't want to hug them. After all this was Ganges. There were standards.

Soon after, the two instructors, Petty Officer Jury and Leverett, who was still only an acting petty officer, treated them to a day out at Clacton as a reward for their efforts. Whether they paid for the outing themselves or if Ganges had a fund set aside for the '*top class*' never entered their heads and none of them thought to ask. One thing was for certain: they *were* the 'top class', they had passed out top-of-the-tree. They didn't know that there was a run ashore up for grabs, or indeed if there was such a thing.

They were just pleased to receive some recognition and what better way was there to accept that recognition than to spend a day at the seaside and be allowed to do their own thing.

It seemed obvious really that every successive recruitment must have had a top class but whether they were rewarded in a similar manner, or if this was something unique to Hawke's 61 and 62 classes because they had 'done so well' no one knew. The only thing that held any significance whatsoever for them was they were going on a day out. A day out, away from Ganges. Away from bugle calls, away from inspections, away from parades, and away from Batchelor.

They trooped down to the boat jetty as soon as breakfast was over and they could get changed into their best suits. Down Faith, Hope and Charity, the trio of stone steps that led down to the foreshore; stone steps that they had cause to dread throughout their year long incarceration; stone steps that they had traversed in both directions many times – and at the double, for some minor infringement. Now they were sauntering down, laughing and joking with each other as they went. They were old hands; they had taken everything Ganges could throw at them; they were heading for a run ashore and pretty soon they would be going to sea.

The Ganges picket boat was waiting for them at the boat jetty and, bolstered up with high spirits, they clambered aboard and headed for Harwich on the other side of the river. The trip over was reminiscent of the time when they were headed for HMS Obdurate. That was several months back and it was cold and wet then and they were heading into the unknown. This time it was bright and sunny despite being early and there were no oilskins to contend with. They were in their new sea-suits and were heading for a day out. The instructors, Jury and Leverett were with them but neither acted like a Ganges instructor. They hardly spoke at all and allowed the boys the concession of being treated like grown-ups. That was a nice gesture and they reciprocated by not racing about or acting in a rowdy manner.

A coach was waiting for them on the Harwich side and, once all were safely aboard, it whisked them away to the anticipated delights of Clacton.

Ginger had never been to Clacton before. Other than a day trip out to London Zoo with his school and the Navy medical in Whitehall, he had never been so far south. Clacton was a strange kind of seaside place. There was no beach or, if there was they missed it, not that they would have wanted to spend much time on a beach in their newly acquired sea suits in any case. They didn't find the town centre either, not that they were particularly keen to find it; after all it would be the shopping area and they were not inclined to part with what little money they had on shopping. Runs ashore for trinkets and souvenirs to take home to mum were something that they hadn't been introduced to at that stage in their career and was well into the future.

What did attract their attention were the Fun Fair and the penny arcade. Those places had the same effect on the boys as a honey pot has on a bee and they spent a couple of happy hours dispensing their meagre amount of cash into the ever-greedy machines. Ginger speculated a portion of his wealth on one such machine and was rewarded with a badge. He was quite happy with his badge and proudly walked around with it pinned to his cap tally until someone pointed out that it displayed a picture of the King – and that the Queen had been on the throne for well in excess of a year. That summed up Clacton of the mid-nineteen fifties: a sleepy little backwater resort, well off the beaten track and still set well and truly in the past.

However, not all of Clacton or its residents came from the same mould, as they were to find out when it was time for tea. By mid afternoon, Leverett and Jury put in an appearance and called everyone together. The bulk of them were not hard to find as they were still in the proximity of that penny arcade and the ornamental gardens. Then, having trooped round to pick up stragglers, the two instructors shepherded them toward a seaside café that, unbeknown to the boys, they had pre booked for them all to have a fish and chips tea.

That café was deceptively large inside and it needed to be, when around fifty boys and two instructors descended on the place. An upstairs room had been prepared especially for them and they were ushered in to take their place on an enormous table that took up all the centre of the room. It was either a very large table or, more likely several put together. Covered by a white tablecloth, who could tell? Either way it was adequate to the task in hand.

As soon as they were seated, smiling waitresses in black and white uniforms placed a steaming hot plate of fish and chips in front of each of them. Plates of bread and butter and salt and vinegar were already at intervals along the table. They served the meal with a smile and an occasional friendly word and that meant a lot to the boys. It was a refreshing change after Ganges treatment. It was something that they were not accustomed to but something they would be very happy to become accustomed to.

A day out; a lovely sunny day; a day of freedom; a first class meal and waitresses that treated them like young gentlemen. They couldn't have asked for more.

After the delights of Clacton, Ganges seemed dull and morbid. Even the anticipation of their impending draft failed to brighten up the place. They had been walking on air straight after their '*finals*' and the whole place had taken on an atmosphere of sweetness and light but now it had reverted to its usual gruesome overtones once again. It appeared that nobody wanted them and it felt that they had become something of an embarrassment.

No one knew what to do with them. There were no classes and there were no Divisions. They could hardly attend Divisions. They had been at the front as senior class and had been centre of attention. Now other classes had moved up to assume that position and there was nowhere for them to go. They couldn't stay at the front, their time was over and they could hardly start at the rear again. They were not wanted. From feeling 'Cock o' the North' – or East to be accurate, they now felt they were yesterday's men; dejected and rejected. All made up and nowhere to go.

They were employed doing menial tasks around the establishment. Tasks such as picking up bits of paper, a job that had already been done by the workship class, or sweeping roads that didn't need sweeping. Some of them were dispatched to various offices and departments where the occupants were expected to find them work. Others even got to go to the married quarters. That was not anywhere near as much fun as it could have been because they were under orders not to talk to any of the occupants and they were reluctant to do so in any case, not knowing who the husband might be, or whether he was at home.

They had been told during their Shotley Routine encounter months ago that a plum job was up at the Captain's house and although none of them ever got near the place then, they learned that it was still on the agenda and a few of them found themselves detailed off for that undertaking, which was a few miles away from Ganges.

Captain, the Earl Cairns was a very nice man. He was a kindly man and not what they expected an establishment Captain to be like. On the rare occasion that he ever spoke to any of the boys he appeared to be interested and always spoke with politeness. Those lucky enough to get to his home, Ewarton Hall, found that this was the man and, if anything, he was even friendlier away from the disciplined atmosphere of Ganges.

Ginger was never fortunate enough to get to the Captain's house but those that did were treated to a slap-up tea at the end of the day courtesy of the Earl and the Countess.

Two or three days were the limit of their wandering about and looking for unnecessary work to do. With a bit of thought they could have let the boys away for a few days leave until their draft came through but that was not the Ganges way. Instead they waited in anticipation for a draft list to appear inside Nelson Hall, the drill shed. They had been told that such a list would be going up, and almost hourly one of their number would check for its arrival. When it was posted there was an excited scramble to see which ship would be the fortunate recipient of the best that Ganges could offer. Ginger was assigned HMS Implacable. He didn't know what Implacable was but his old mate Mick Southern was also heading there and Mick knew that it was an aircraft carrier. Several others were also heading for Implacable. So that was to be his destiny.

TEN

On the one hand time seemed to stand still for them and everything appeared to be in slow motion but, at the same time, things were happening at breakneck speed. Their time was over, their course was run and on the last day of May, one year and twenty-six days after they first set foot on Ganges soil, they bid farewell to the place – hopefully for good – and headed for a life on the ocean wave at long last.

With all their exams, tests, finals, inspections and any other poking and prodding Ganges could think of to inflict them with behind them, the entire atmosphere of the place seemed to change. The weather was warm and sunny, just like it was when Ginger stepped off that coach for the first time just over a year earlier. This time the entire establishment appeared to be lighter and brighter and he could sense a distinct feeling of freedom in the air. It seemed to be everywhere and he felt sure that the others felt it to. No one had said anything out of the ordinary to them but somehow they now felt different. Even the buildings had lost their foreboding look and, for the first time he could see things in their true perspective and without the underlying fear and uncertainties that had dogged him for the previous twelve months. Their time was over; they had *'done their bit'* and now they felt that they no longer belonged. It was time to get out of there.

The kitbags that they had so carefully packed and their hammocks that were lashed up to perfection, courtesy of Batchelor, had been stacked up under the colonnade and they made their way to the end of Nelson Hall to muster before making their way down Faith, Hope and Charity for the last time and onto the boat jetty for the Ganges picket boat to take them across to Harwich and the train for London.

If there was anyone among them who harboured pangs of regret at leaving they kept it to themselves and, as far as Ginger could make out, there was not a teardrop or a sad face to be seen. For his own part the earlier euphoria was still affecting him and he couldn't even be bothered to look round for a last sight of the place as they ploughed through the water

They were out of there and this time for good. It was a much better feeling than when they went on leave. Leave was lovely. It got them out of that place for three glorious weeks. Three weeks without continually being on your guard all the time. Three weeks of no shouting and bullying. Three weeks without instruction all day and every day. Three weeks to do more or less as you pleased. That certainly was a good feeling and one that every one of them looked forward to. But this time it was even better: this time they would not be coming back!

Leverett was waiting for them at Harwich station. Where he had appeared from was a bit of a mystery, they hadn't been expecting him; he must have been on the boat with them, although he had been very quiet. Ginger's heart sank. He hadn't thought about who would show them the way through London and take them to where their connection for the south coast went from. It had never occurred to him although now it made sense. Of course they would need a guide but why did it have to be Leverett of all people.

Just catching sight of Leverett brought an uncomfortable feeling with it, he had that effect on them. He stood glaring, his blue suit pressed, his hat shoved right down to his ears as usual, his face red and his veins still inflated although there was no reason. Ginger lost himself in among the multitude, putting as many people as possible between him and Leverett.

That was a wise move as it turned out because straight away the kitbags and hammocks turned up and were dumped on the platform. After passengers had alighted from the train that had just arrived, Leverett ordered: 'Bags and hammocks into the goods van then. Chop-chop.'

By luck, or possibly because they had done it so many times in the past that they knew, the pile of bags and hammocks were right where the goods van stopped. From the safety of behind his erstwhile messmates, Ginger watched Dereham leap forward and start loading them into the open door, eagerly looking at Leverett for praise. A couple of others who were a bit too close to ignore Leverett's orders reluctantly helped him while the rest of them piled into the train carriages to find themselves a good seat.

Good old Dereham did the work, humping the kit about for them, still looking for praise from Leverett. It appeared that he hadn't learned very much during the previous twelve months after all.

Then, having arrived at Liverpool Street Station and after a bit of shuffling around and trying not to get separated from the others, under the guidance of Leverett and with no time to see the sights of London, they embarked on another train that would take them south to Portland and their new home, HMS Implacable.

Apart from the one-day trip to London for his medical, before joining up and the short journeys from Ipswich to Norwich for leave from Ganges, Ginger had never been on a long train journey and everything south of London, or south of Ipswich for that matter, was new territory for him.

The coast bound train carriage was open plan, which meant Leverett was never far away, although he said very little. He was a different man than the

Leverett they knew from yesterday and the year before that. Ginger was enjoying the trip. There was a map of the journey in a frame on the partition wall and he delighted in counting off the stations as they made their way south. The atmosphere was relaxed as they sped to their destination, despite having to keep a wary eye on Leverett. He was as happy as he had been on the Sunday-School outings to the seaside he had enjoyed with his schoolmates a few years previously.

Now he had new mates and this was all exciting stuff. He had never been so far before. He recalled a day out they'd had in HMS Obdurate sometime ago during their Ganges year. That time he had written to his mum telling her that they had been to sea and way out to within sight of France. Actually he wasn't sure if he had seen France or not and most probably not but he had been to sea on a ship and the excitement had got to him, despite the inclement weather. It had rained hard all that day so, if he had happened to see a bit of coastline, there would have been no telling if it was France or a bit of Felixstowe.

It never occurred to him that all this travel he was getting excited about was small potatoes really because everywhere he had travelled so far was soon to be eclipsed by real travel and, in the not too distant future, it was bound to be world travel at that.

Petty Officer Leverett had them organised almost as the train drew to a halt at Weymouth station. Their bags and hammocks were unceremoniously heaved out onto the platform in a big heap. Once again Dereham did the honours; he still hadn't learned. Still he looked to Leverett for praise but Leverett had no interest in them any more. His job was over; they were not his responsibility any longer. He was in a hurry suddenly almost as if he had somewhere important to go.

From there it was onto a coach and it was not long before they were topping the rise that led down to Portland Bay. It was a lovely vantage point and a sight to behold. There were several ships out in the half circular bay. It was the most ships Ginger had ever seen before and it would have been nice to have stopped to admire them for a while. But all too soon they were down at the waters edge of Portland harbour, with their bags and hammocks in an old wooden shed at the inshore end of a short pier – and Leverett was gone. He didn't *formally* hand them over and he didn't say goodbye, as PO Jury would have done. He just drifted away and it was some time before they were aware that he wasn't there any more.

The man waiting to meet them was a three badge petty officer. He was short and slight in appearance but his most noticeable feature was his insistence in calling hammocks 'hammicks'. The little man was a bundle of nervous energy and didn't seem able to stand still. He talked loud and fast in a high pitched voice and, perhaps because it was alien to their ears, he appeared to use the word 'hammicks' rather too often. He also appeared to have no teeth, which made his voice sound a bit sloppy and spitty. Ginger had already assumed his usual position behind the bulk of his travelling companions so he was not in a position to see if the man had teeth or not and he was not interested enough to move closer for a better look.

By the time *Mr Hammick* had finished fussing about, a Motor Fishing Vessel (MFV) had come alongside the pier and, this time, they had to carry their own kitbag and hammock aboard and off again when they reached their destination. They learned that the MFV was the tender for whatever ships were in the harbour, ferrying people and stores to the various ships that were all anchored out in the bay.

The trip across to Implacable brought back memories of that Obdurate episode yet again. Ginger couldn't help but remember. It was horrible but this time the ride was quite pleasant; it was June the first after all and the sun was shining. Not like the pouring rain they endured on that particular trip. Although that, in its way, was an adventure. That was his first time on a boat and his first time on a ship for that matter. Plus, of course, this time they were heading for a ship that was to become their home and not just a day visit.

Their transport slid gently alongside Implacable's gangway and someone ordered: 'Up bag and hammock and up yer go then!'

That gangway was a long way up from the platform at the bottom end but Ginger was not about to show any fear, despite being a bit top heavy with his kitbag on his shoulder. Once on it and away up he found that it was safe enough, very much like uncarpeted stairs and far more stable than it looked from the bottom.

From the top of the gangway they were shepherded into the upper hangar, where a section had been corralled of with canvas to about waist high, just for them. No change here then, thought Ginger. What happened to the bit about how they were men now and ready for sea? They were first class; they were Tiddly Jack; they were top of the heap. They had been through Ganges and had passed out top of the tree. Everyone knew that, everyone had watched them. They were the cat's whiskers. They had done well in their passing out results. They had been congratulated. They had been told they were now ready to join the Fleet. They had come from the place from where the men for the Fleet were drafted. They were on a ship, a warship, a man-o'-war. They had come to join the Fleet. They were ready and willing and now they were being herded into a section specially designated for the accommodation of boys.

They had completed a year at Ganges and had left with their heads held high. Now they had finally made it onto a proper ship and were ready to be integrated into the ships company. But instead they were being treated like boys again. However, the reason for what appeared to be their segregation soon became clear. It was late in the afternoon and they had missed their dinner and teatime. Implacable was being kind to them. They were boys from Ganges so it went without saying that they would be hungry. Ganges boys were always hungry. Inside their temporary canvas home they were lashed up to egg and chips. Naturally the egg was cold and the chips were over greasy but with a chunk of bread and a mug of tea it was a welcome meal, appreciated and scoffed in true Ganges fashion.

After their welcome meal they were escorted to their new home: the boys' mess. The boys' mess deck was a long way down and a long way aft and just forward of the lower hangar. They threaded their way down the passages, follow-the-leader, conger style, until they reached their destination.

Inside a chief GI met them. He told them he was their new instructor. He was a tall thin man and spoke with a rather high-pitched voice. He had a strange look on his face that gave him an embarrassed look. Ginger gave him the 'once-over' from the comparative safety of behind other peoples shoulders and deduced that that look was a mixture of the tough image that all GIs try to portray while, at the same time, trying to smile in an attempt to put them at ease. What he achieved was to make himself look mildly ridiculous.

It was early days yet and not enough time to get a true picture of the man. Ginger thought back to their first meeting with Petty Officer Leverett at Ganges when he had escorted them over to Hawke Division, from the Annexe. Their first impressions of him were exactly correct. But this man was harder to read. Sure enough he was a GI and a chief at that. GIs liked to portray a tough image, it was in-built into their system by the time they had that badge on their right arm. This early encounter suggested that he had never been an instructor at Ganges. He was trying to be kind; he was trying to be polite and, at the same time, he was trying to remain aloof and retain his Gunnery Instructor posture. There was no way that he could do all three.

'Place all hammocks in the hammock netting over there,' he said, indicating with his arm. 'Then find yourselves a locker, put a bit of kit in it and leave the rest to be unpacked later.' His voice suited his appearance. Now that they were getting used to him they noticed other little mannerisms. He spoke in a singsong kind of way and that half smile remained in place even as he spoke. As he turned his head, the top half of his body followed; it looked as if he had left the coat hanger in his jacket.

The first time he tried out one of his 'parade ground' type orders almost spelt disaster for the boys. They didn't want to upset him for no reason but it hurt to suppress laughter when he called them to attention for the first time. The high-pitched tone of his voice, coupled with the singsong quality that would not have been out of place in a comic opera, combined to test the boys. They struggled to keep a straight face as he sang out: Hiiinneeeee!

That one word order seemed to go on for some time and drifted off quieter toward the end. They had learned not to show any emotion during their Ganges incarceration and had coped well but just that one word took all their will power not to laugh out loud.

He had told them to find a locker and that was their next move. The lockers were in a room of their own and a few steps down from the messdeck. The heads (toilets) were also down lower than the main mess. It seemed that the entire mess had been created at a later date and long after the ship had been built and sort of stuck in an empty space. At the back of the mess were steps leading down to the lower hangar. There were no aeroplanes on board and the lower hangar was used as extra storage for everything that didn't have a stowage anywhere else. In the passage outside the mess door was the laundry and opposite the laundry the bakery. Nearby was the galley so there was not far to go to pick up their meals. After that first meal having been delivered to them, they were now expected to look after themselves and collect their own meals and wash up after, they were told.

After their new chief had finished his little welcome to Implacable pep talk, the next thing he told them, was to find the Regulating Office and complete a 'joining routine'.

Implacable was a big ship with a maze of passages everywhere and it appeared to have ladders and hatchways in all directions and wherever one looked. Every hatch, every ladder, every passage looked the same and it was simplicity itself to take a wrong turning or head up a wrong ladder and find oneself completely lost.

Eventually the Regulating Office was located, thanks to some first class navigation by a couple of front-runners but that was nowhere near the end of their problems. Joining routine completed and station cards issued, they were then dispatched to the Sick Bay and after that the Pay Office before being directed to their divisional office for another pep talk, this time from their new divisional officer.

Time was getting on by the time they had *officially* become members of the ships company and, back on the messdeck the chief told them to wander off and explore the ship, 'to get your bearings', he said. That was a lot easier said than done. Several of them were already coming the 'old hand routine' and leading the way, because 'they knew'. But the old ship, that they were told had fought the Japanese in the Pacific, had lots of secrets and she was not about to surrender them all at once to a bunch of greenhorn nozzers. In and out of endless passages they went, up and down ladders, through hatches and watertight doors, until someone acknowledged that they had no idea of what they were doing or where they were going.

Ginger was one of the first to concede that enough was enough. It was all a great adventure to be allowed to roam about on a ship without supervision and, on occasion, it was refreshing that when they did run into someone there was no third degree into what they were doing or why they were there. But, he figured, there has to come a time when going up and down the same passages and ladders lost its novelty and a quiet sit down would be of greater value. After all it had been quite an eventful day.

Back on the messdeck some of them hadn't bothered to go exploring or had given up and returned early. When Ginger went in he was surprised to see several of them already there. He thought that he might have been on his own, for a while at least. But it wasn't long before everyone had come back and soon after that the chief returned.

He suggested that the hammocks they had put in the fenced of area that he said was called the hammock netting when they first came into the mess, should now be 'slung'. It was a suggestion rather than an order and when they complied, the chief stayed with them and showed them how to sling their hammocks and where to sling them from hammock bars suspended from the deckhead. He demonstrated how to undo the lashing and coil it up neatly by the nettles at the head and how to sort out the mattress.

But even then it was not all plain sailing. None of them had ever slept in a hammock before and just getting in required quite a feat of acrobatics, as many of them found when they threw their legs up, just like the chief told them, to land on the deck right over the other side. Then it became apparent why there were so many nettles on the end of their hammock. Carefully adjusted, those sixteen nettles, some made shorter and some left longer, gave the hammock an open aspect. As theirs were all the same length it left the hammock closed almost as if it was still lashed up and most difficult to climb into.

The chief patiently showed them which bars to hang their hammock from and which others to use to help swing themselves in and after a few attempts and a bit of good natured chafing, plus one or two choice words, they finally settled down to sleep.

Almost as soon as they were awoken in the morning the chief was there at their side showing them how to lash-up correctly. They didn't let on that Batchelor had already instructed them in that art and, in any case, the chief was a far more friendly and approachable man. He helped several of them that were having difficulties. Ginger managed his unaided although the finished article looked more like a sack of potatoes than a correctly lashed-up hammock 'a la Batchelor'.

Then it was case of wash, dress in the rig of the day and standby for breakfast. Chief detailed two of them to go to the galley and get the breakfast and the remainder to get the plates, cutlery and cups out. This was new to them. This was the first time they had to collect their own meal from the galley, dish it out on to the required amount of plates, and wash up and stow away everything afterward. It was quite an evolution and Ginger noticed that it was Shavers, their parade marker from Ganges who had the honour of the first washing up. Their first washing-up ever. It was an historic moment although judging by the look on Shaver's face, a moment he would gladly have foregone.

Their first muster was in the upper hangar. It was not as formal as Ganges Divisions. It was designed to get everybody into one place to detail them off for the parts of ship work. Being new boys, all eyes were on them and they were the first to receive their marching orders. Some to the quarterdeck, some to the forecastle, others to here there and everywhere. Ginger was assigned to the heads, the ships company toilets. He really drew the short straw.

As the Chief Buffer detailed him he gestured with his arm to where a chap in overalls beckoned for him to follow. 'Overalls' seemed friendly enough. He was young looking and couldn't have been much older than Ginger. As they walked away he started straight into his spiel. 'You'll be OK with me. It's an easy job. I'll look after you....'

He continued with a stream of unnecessary clichés and platitudes all the way to their destination. Friendly was one thing but he was getting far too friendly too quickly; pretty soon Ginger felt that he would want to be holding hands. That thought was not far from the truth.

The ships company heads was an enormous place with rows and rows of cubicles and just enough room to walk between rows.

Now they were on their own Overalls said: 'I'll just have a quick check that there's nothing blocked up, then we have to tidy up the cleaning stores caboose and check the stores.'

Ginger didn't know what a cleaning stores caboose was or for that matter where it was. Stores suggested a cupboard and as it looked like a cupboard at the far end, he ventured up to check it out. It was a cupboard, it was a very small room with cleaning materials on a couple of shelves and buckets and mops on the deck.

As he stood looking in, with the door open, he felt Overalls close behind him.

'That's right, you found it then,' he almost purred rubbing his hand up and down inside Gingers rolled up shirtsleeve. 'You seem like a nice boy,' he continued. 'I'll ask for you again tomorrow.'

Ginger was pretty naïve but even his naivety couldn't help but understand where this was leading. That penny dropped in double record time. Luckily, just then somebody came in. They heard him rather than saw him but that was enough to have Overalls pull back. Ginger grabbed a mop and ran down to the far end, 'Er, I thought I saw a puddle,' he mumbled over his shoulder.

He was in a quandary. It was early days, only his first day on the ship, and he was still affected by Ganges conditioning. At Ganges if any of them got themselves into a head-to-head confrontation with instructors or ships company there was only ever going to be one person in the wrong and he felt this could easily end up the same. Who would they believe? The new boy or a ships company member that everyone knew? He couldn't even ask for a job change because they would want to know why and what could he say? On their ship for less than twenty-four hours and already a troublemaker.

He took his time with the imaginary puddle, willing someone else to come in but, in what seemed like an eternity, the place remained empty. He was alone with Overalls again. Overalls was nowhere to be seen. Ginger decided to return his mop, after all there was only so much he could do with a mop on a dry deck.

But as he opened the caboose door, 'Overalls was waiting inside. 'You've been a long time,' he said. 'Come in and shut the door. I want to talk to you. I'll ask for you again tomorrow.' He had his overall buttons undone from top to the very bottom, all down the front.

Ginger didn't know what to do. He figured that whatever the outcome it was going to be him that would be in the wrong. It would get turned around so that it was all his fault. Overalls was so close that there wasn't room to move and he was rubbing his arms again.

Ginger was panicking big time. Overalls was so close that he couldn't move in that small cupboard and still he was stroking and rubbing his arms. He was in deep. Maybe he should have said something earlier but there was never a clear-cut moment, it had all happened quickly but at the same time gradually.

Suddenly something seemed to explode. Ginger could take no more. If he could have ran he would but he was trapped. Without thinking it through he snatched his knee up with all the force that he could muster and, just as suddenly, Overalls was coughing and choking in front of him. Then it was panic time again. What had he done. How could he get out of this one. This meant *jankers* and lots of it. Overalls was still gasping for breath.

Then everything became crystal clear and appeared to go into slow motion. Ginger didn't care about *jankers*. He didn't give a thought for the ship. He was there on his own and no one would believe him anyway. As Overalls gasped for air, he was leaning forward, doubled over. As he leaned forward Ginger, cold, calm and calculated, sized him up and, bending his knees slightly, hit him on the point of his chin with all the force and contempt that he could muster. Straightening his legs at the same time lent extra impetus to the blow and Overalls crumpled into a heap without a sound.

The calmness still surrounded him as he opened the caboose door and stepped out. There was no one in sight but Ginger didn't care. He was calm. Maybe it was the calm before the storm but at that moment he was calm. He made his way to the upper hangar and then up again and out onto the flight deck. There was hardly anyone on the flight deck but he didn't want anyone to talk to anyway.

He passed his time between the flight deck and the upper hangar right around until dinnertime. He missed his stand-easy mid-morning cup of tea because he didn't want the chief to ask him how he was getting on. At dinnertime nothing was mentioned and nothing of the episode was ever mentioned. The Chief Buffer never asked him to go back and he never saw Overalls again. Maybe he fell in the heads and had to go to hospital. Who knows? Ginger didn't care. He fully expected jankers over the incident and when he didn't get any, he was quids in.

If anyone in authority did know what had happened it was never relayed to Ginger. It must have been doubtful if anything had ever been said because it would have been turned into a major production with him as the star performer. The Navy was not geared to let sleeping dogs lie.

The next morning at the muster in the upper hangar, the Chief Buffer detailed him off for boats crew. The order was made in a matter-of-fact manner and with nothing personal in it at all. They wanted a boy for the pinnace and here was one right next to him. He showed no signs of recognition and, apart from giving him a slight shove to start him on his way, showed no interest in him at all. Ginger was still on tenterhooks; it was early days yet and things could still take a turn for the worse but, at the moment, it looked as if Overalls had kept the incident to himself.

The first thing to be done was to change into a blue suit and plimsoles and then report to the lower boom where the pinnace was tied up. The crew were waiting for him when he arrived. He was to be the new bowman. Still comparing everything to Ganges routine, he was expecting an interrogation into why it had taken him so long although he had changed and rushed back in double quick time. Instead, although they were waiting for him, they appeared to be in no hurry to go anywhere.

Ginger looked over the guardrails above the pinnace half expecting a lot of shouting and venom. Instead the cox'n spotted him and with a wave of his hand, indicating where he should go, called out: 'Hello lad. Along the boom and down the ladder with you then.'

There was none of the attitude he would have expected at Ganges, turning up to strangers for the first time: where have you been? What took you so long? Why is the seawater so wet? Do you need a haircut? No. Quite the reverse. These two people seemed pleased to see him.

The cox'n was a short tubby fair-haired chap of, maybe thirty. A leading hand. He had a soft tone of voice which put Ginger at ease right away. At first acquaintance he appeared friendly enough. His number two was a younger curly haired chap who laughed a lot and came out with silly sayings and light-hearted remarks almost non-stop.

Ginger clambered into the boat from the Jacobs-ladder hanging from the boom. He had never done that before and he prayed that he wouldn't disgrace himself by falling off or making a hash of things.

He didn't know whether he should speak or not but he could hardly stand there and say nothing. He thought he would test the water.

'Good morning.'

'Yeh, good morning, lad. You're the new bowman. Take your position up in the bows and we'll be off.'

That was it. No pep talk. No threats. No shouting. He was in. He was doing a man's job. He was boats crew, just like a real sailor. This was the life.

Unfortunately the boats crew episode didn't last long. A couple of days later and as soon as they weighed anchor his job came to an end. There was no explanation; there were no goodbyes. At sea there was no use for a boat or a boats crew. The crew had a quiet number when at sea, hanging around the boat or losing themselves in the odd cubbyholes that they had made their own. They didn't want some boy hanging around and drawing attention to them.

About half of the boys from Hawke 49 mess had come to Implacable, about equal numbers from 61 and 62 classes. They all appeared to have been assigned to part-of-ship duties such as cleaning brass-work, scrubbing the quarterdeck, scrubbing passages etc. Ginger seemed to be the odd one out. He was continually aware of his *'green-coat status'* and had tried to always remain in the background. He had been singled out but as far as he knew it was nothing personal. It was simply sod's law of being in the wrong place at the wrong time. On the other hand it was better than scrubbing and painting on the upper deck.

So it was that for his next move he found himself in the laundry. The laundry was just up the passage from the boys' mess. A staff of three manned it. A leading hand who could easily have passed as the boat cox'n's twin brother, a chap that hardly ever spoke and 'Tex'. Tex was a tall thin torpedoman. He was the strangest man you could ever meet. He acted like he was a cowboy. A cowboy with attitude. Tex never had a kind word for anyone. It was a miracle that he still had all his teeth. It was a wonder he still had his life.

Ginger's job was easy. He had to undo the bundles as they came in and check that every piece had the owner's laundry number on it in the prescribed place. If not then to write it on with a small pen and marking ink. The good thing about working in the laundry was that he got all his washing done for nothing. He was told that if he had anything to wash, just to chuck it in with a load of the same colour at any time. He didn't need a second invitation and in a very short space of time his entire kit, apart from his blue suits, had been through the system for free.

All went well with the laundry until he was asked to make tea one afternoon. The laundry staff had their own little mess room near the boys' mess door and although Ginger still had his meals in his mess and slept there, he spent quite a bit of time in that little mess room during the day. They were allowed to draw extra rations of tea because it was deemed thirsty work working in the laundry.

Ginger had never made tea before. He knew that you put a handful of tea into the pot and topped it up with hot water but, as he had not had a turn as cook of the mess he didn't know where the hot water came from. He figured that being a laundry there was bound to be hot water there all the time. So he went in and filled the teapot up from under the hot tap.

Luckily it was the chap that didn't say much who tried it first and not Tex. Even so, Ginger had never heard him say so much all at once and none of it complimentary. The contents of that teapot went down the sink in the washhouse and a fresh brew was made. He wasn't offered one and the next day he noticed that one of the two Moor's, the one who had been in the Bugle Band at Ganges, was sitting at the laundry mess table in what used to be his place.

At the afternoon muster the following day, the Chief Buffer announced that the dentist needed a messenger and for some uncanny reason Ginger was singled out again. He had spent the forenoon wandering about on the forecastle, mainly keeping out of everyone's way and had decided that anything was better than being up there on a regular basis. It was cold, wet and very windy, right at the front, just under the end of the flight deck. It was a horrible place to have to work and spend a lot of time.

He had had quite a bit of dealings with dentists, courtesy of Ganges, so he was familiar with the surroundings. He didn't like dentists but this time it wasn't to be him in the hot seat. The dentists' rooms were just inside the door that led out onto the flight deck.

Ginger gave a timid little knock on the door and, as there was no response, he opened it a little and peered inside. It was a waiting room. An SBA in the next room heard him enter and came to investigate.

'I'm your new messenger,' he began. He thought it prudent not to treat people as friendly until it had been established that they were. 'I've been sent -' he continued before being cut off.

'Yes, OK then,' the SBA said. He picked up a pile of papers and handed them to Ginger. They were large internal mail envelopes. 'The department name, or the person they're to go to is the last name on the front. OK. Away you go then.' As an afterthought he added quietly: 'Take your time. You won't need to come back any more today. See you tomorrow.'

Ginger thanked him for the time off and departed on his mission. There were six envelopes addressed to various bods and some just to departments. It was just as well he had been given the rest of the afternoon to deliver them. He had no idea who or where they were. After wandering about as if in a trance for over an hour, looking on doors for a clue and getting nowhere and still clutching the same six envelopes, he was forced to throw caution to the wind and take a chance on asking someone for directions.

After that it was a piece of cake. Having been directed to the first one, he then asked in turn for directions to the next one and all were safely delivered with time to spare. Three of those visited handed him similar envelopes to be delivered elsewhere but he was having none of that. Not until he had a better idea of the layout of the ship and certainly not this close to teatime. He mumbled something to the effect of being required urgently on the bridge and made a hasty exit before any questions could be asked.

He dismissed himself from the morning muster the next day when special dutymen was called for. He didn't know if he was a special dutyman or not but no one questioned or tried to stop him. He was eager to be getting on with his new job. Messenger was easy – you could almost do what you liked. His first job of the day was to go to the flammable store and get the dentist's paraffin can filled. The SBA handed him the can and gave him directions.

When he returned with the filled can the SBA was not in the waiting room so he opened the next door and was faced with the dentist and a man that he had in the chair.

'Get out of here!' bellowed the dentist, 'You can't come barging in here like that.' Ginger didn't get the chance to apologise or say anything. He didn't know. He thought it was the SBA's office. He closed the door and returned to the waiting room where he sat with his can until the SBA came back and took it from him.

Half an hour later the part-of-ship chief from the quarterdeck came looking for him.

'Follow me,' he ordered.

He didn't say where they were going but Ginger guessed. He had had the good fortune to have been given four quiet numbers and he had cocked up with each of them. The dentists must have been the last chance and he had managed to bugger that up as well.

As he marched along, following the chief to places unknown, he wasn't feeling sad or dejected. It was a lot better than Ganges. He'd been on board a few days and, really, he hadn't done a thing. Life was good and getting better all the time.

Their feet sounded a bit hollow and made a slight slapping sound as they walked. Ginger tried to get half a pace out of step with the chief, who was unaware of what was going on, to give an extra beat to their rhythm. It seemed to be saying: 'Watch out quarterdeck, here I come!'

128

ELEVEN

Implacable was good, it was a lot better and much easier than Ganges. They were still boys and they were treated as such to some respect, but life was a whole lot easier and the icing on the cake came on payday, when they received the princely sum of two pounds. They thought they were the cat's whiskers when their pay went up by half-a-crown to seven shillings and sixpence when they attained first class status at Ganges. But this was something else, it was quite unexpected and in a different league altogether.

Ginger came away from the Paybob's table and stood admiring the two pound notes they had given him. There had been no mention of any raise in pay; he couldn't believe his good fortune, two whole pounds. Fair enough, they had now joined the ship's pay cycle and that meant they would get paid every two weeks in future, rather than the weekly payday that had been accustomed to at Ganges but even then it was still a considerable raise. From seven shillings and sixpence to a pound a week. Overnight his pay had more than doubled and, in fact, had almost trebled.

Almost in the centre of the ship was a large open space. To some extent it was similar to one of those shopping malls that had begun to find their way over from America. On the port side was a purpose built barbers shop with two chairs and two full time barbers in attendance. On the opposite side was bookshop and stationery shop. There were a few more little 'shops' with their stable type half-doors open, each one complete with a NAAFI man ready to relieve him of his new-found wealth. Ginger was like the proverbial kid-in-a-sweet-shop. He had that much money, he didn't know what to do with it.

In the flat directly below was a Goffa Bar, with yet another NAAFI man dispensing ice creams and fruit juices to all and sundry, across his little bar. He, just the same as his colleagues in the flat above, was ready and willing to relieve them of as much as he possibly could.

Those *'goffas'* were some kind of fruit juices and were very tasty but an *'ice-cream goffa'* was something else and out of this world. It was one of the varieties of fruit juice with a scoop of ice cream in the top and whisked up into froth with an electric whisk; they were absolutely delicious and irresistible.

Ginger had never encountered so much luxury. There were very few, if any, luxuries at Ganges and even less at home before he had joined up.

They had only just emerged from austere times brought about by the war and many things were still rationed when he joined. His mother was a frugal sort of woman and possibly things were not quite as difficult to come by, as she would lead them to believe. However, she was not there. It was certain that she wouldn't have approved of him 'wasting money' but he was in his element. It was like Aladdin's cave and, for the first time ever, he felt unrestricted. There was no Batchelor to spoil his moment and there was no duty petty officer to tell him to hurry up and move on. There was a real feeling of wellbeing, he felt good and took his time just wandering about and looking at things. He didn't want to buy anything specific; he was mesmerised by the array of things on display …. and he was about to fill his boots.

With a week or two on a ship under his belt and a little money in his pocket, things could not get much better and, as time progressed, Ginger felt comfortable with himself and his surroundings. He had messed up on those quiet numbers he'd been assigned but nobody seemed to hold that against him. He was the loser and no one else was interested. He had had a couple of days on the quarterdeck where Mick Southern and a couple of others were. That wasn't as much fun as being in the laundry with almost nothing to do but even then he had landed on his feet. Because, on his second morning, after having been taken there from the dentists, by the quarterdeck chief the day before, he was ordered by a petty officer to go and draw some new holes for a hammock netting, from the stores. Somewhere in the back of his mind Ginger recalled something someone had once told them about sending idiot boys all over the ship for weird and wonderful items like 'green oil for the starboard lights and red oil for the port lights' …. 'and don't get them mixed up!' but he played along. That petty officer reminder him of Leverett when he tried to get people to laugh at some cruel joke of his.

The sniggering gave the game away but Ginger pretended not to notice and innocently went on his mission. He had no idea where the stores office was. But that could wait. First, he had the best part of the day off. If they could play games, so could he.

There was a type of theatrical stage at one end of the upper hangar, and quite by accident some days earlier, he had found himself up a wrong ladder and in behind the stage. He figured that would be where to head for again to lose himself for a couple of hours. He was in no hurry and took his time just wandering around and was first in the mess for stand-easy and a cup of tea.

He reasoned that his safety lay in the fact that, if anyone should question why he was not working, he could truthfully say that he had been sent to the stores to get holes for the hammock netting. Conversely, if that petty officer should come looking for him he could hardly charge Ginger for wasting time when it was his fault for sending him on a wild goose chase in the first place. With that *'get-out-of-jail-free'* card safely memorised, straight after stand-easy, he made a beeline for that backstage area and snuggled down on some curtains, where he stayed until the Tannoy piped 'hands to dinner'.

Ginger wasn't duty cook of the mess so he was in no great hurry to get down there. As he entered the mess the dishing out of dinners was already under way and there was a new man in charge. He hadn't seen the messdeck chief since early morning and now this new man, a three badge petty officer, had replaced him. The new petty officer was a small man and his three badges and his crossed anchors covered most of the short sleeve of his jacket. He had the most appalling accent. As Ginger entered, he was calling for the mess cloth, which he was referring to as the *'cloorrth'*. Ginger couldn't hazard a guess as to what part of the country this man had originated, although deepest Devon or maybe parts of Cornwall looked to be leading contenders.

He spotted Ginger. 'Ah, who are you? Where have you been?' he asked.

Ginger didn't know if he really wanted to know or if he was just being friendly, as this was the first time they had met. Accordingly he played it cautiously.

'Petty Officer. I've been running errands for the quarterdeck chief.' He told him.

He acknowledged Ginger's answer with a nod and turned his attention elsewhere. The answer appeared to satisfy him, or maybe that was his way to a non-committal introduction. Ginger thanked his lucky stars that he hadn't said too much and, inadvertently, played his *ace-in-the-hole*. That card could still come in handy later; he had no intention of wasting it.

After the dinner break he fell out with the special-duty men. By now they were used to seeing him fall out and no one took any particular notice when he marched swiftly away. He had at least until mid-afternoon stand-easy before he would even attempt to search out the stores office and do his innocent little boy lost *'I've come for holes for the hammock netting, please chief'* routine. He knew that he would be perfectly safe because they liked to play those games and, maybe it would give them all a laugh back in the Chiefs' Mess later. But for once he was ahead of them and he was in a position to play them at their own game. Even if they cottoned on to the fact that he was turning the tables there was nothing to be done about it.

However, hiding away wasn't all it was cracked up to be. It had been great during the forenoon. Those curtains, backstage were as comfortable as his hammock and he may have dozed for short periods occasionally but to go back there again after dinner would probably be pushing his luck a bit too far. Being caught in there was to be caught in a *cul-de-sac* and would, almost certainly, spell big-time trouble. On the other had, just wandering about the passages and by-ways could bring no grief down on him. In any case he still had his *ace-in-the-hole* if things should get a bit sticky.

Keeping away from the 'shopping mall' flat seemed a good plan. Although there were some people in there and others were passing through all the time, he didn't want to attract attention to himself by looking in the windows or stopping to buy anything during working hours. There were lots of the ship that he still didn't know at all and although he ventured into alien areas, just for a quick look, he kept to the places that he knew in the main.

After a stand-easy cup of tea Ginger figured that it was time to give his mission some attention. After all, since about nine o'clock he had not done a thing and this skiving with nothing to do was getting a bit boring. He didn't want to get back to the quarterdeck too early so a last tour of the flight deck and the upper hangar seemed to be in order, after all he still had his '*get-out-of-jail-free*' card in reserve, if he was challenged.

On the stage in the upper hangar a few Royal Marine bandsmen were hanging around the piano. One was sitting at the piano and two or three others were involved with a musical score on the piano stand. It was the strains of their music that brought Ginger into hangar. After a quick check of their sleeves for corporals or sergeants and finding there wasn't any he felt brave enough to approach. He hadn't seen any of them before so the chances were good that they didn't know who he was either. That had to be good news. As he approached, the quartet broke into a modern melody, one that had just become popular and was being played on the radio quite a lot. It was lovely and it took him out of himself. He completely forgot where he was.

An hour and a couple of his favourite Doris Day tunes later, Ginger suddenly remembered his mission. The music had been lovely and a real treat but with the time galloping away he had to scoot. Hell for leather he legged it along passages and down ladders to the 'shopping mall' flat. There was bound to be someone there who could direct him to the stores office.

'Could you tell me where the stores office is please?' he enquired of the first person he saw.

'No idea mate. I'm a stoker,' was the genuine but unhelpful reply. The next reply was just as unhelpful but nowhere near as polite.

Then. 'Stores office? Do you know where it is?'

'Certainly lad. What yer want it for?'

The man had a red badge on his hat and a stores emblem on his right arm. Ginger hadn't noticed right away but now that he had time he realised that he had asked exactly the right person. The question now was, should he tell him the full story. It was fast approaching four o'clock and knocking off time. He had no choice. Listening to those bandsmen, lovely as it was, had put him well behind.

This was going to sound really silly; he was going to lose face but it had to be done. Time was running out.

'Er, I have to see the chief rather urgently,' he said, trying to imply he had something important to impart.

'Well the chief has gone and the place is locked up. If it's urgent perhaps I can help.' The man said, kindly. He was a nice man and he was listening properly to what Ginger was saying. That made it all the more difficult.

'Um .... er .... , I have to enquire about some hammock netting,' he was quite proud of that spur of the moment non-committal answer.

'Ah, I see,' the man said. His face showed that he understood perfectly. 'Have you got a chitty?'

'No I haven't got a chitty. I wasn't given one.' He told him. This was a stupid conversation. Ginger knew it was a load of old twaddle and what's more he knew that the stores man knew it too. But he was forced to play innocent. He had brought it upon himself; he had to play it through.

'Well, without a chitty, we can't do anything today,' the stores man said. 'Best tell whoever sent you that you need a chitty. Bring it back tomorrow. OK lad?'

That put him in a quandary. What was he going to do now? It was almost four o'clock and the only course of action that he could see was to brazen it out. He would just go back to the messdeck and if that quarterdeck PO came looking for him, then bad luck. Otherwise he would sort it out in the morning and face the music then.

He was on edge when he entered the mess. He had waited a few minutes after the Tannoy had signalled that it was time to secure for the day, just so as not to be the first one back. He wasn't the first back. There were several in there and they had already got the teapot on the go. Apart from the usual banter, no one took any particular interest in him as he picked up a cup and helped himself to a cup of tea from the big pot on the table. The mess petty officer was not in the mess and Ginger thought it prudent not to ask if anyone had been looking for him. He figured that if anyone wanted him they would find him soon enough without him drawing attention to himself. But no one said anything and no one came looking for him.

In the morning and back on the quarterdeck, still no one said anything. Although the petty officer who had sent him on his mission was nowhere to be seen, Ginger wondered if the storm would break when he did put in an appearance. But by the end of the day he hadn't set eyes on him and his confidence had been returning as each hour passed. With a full day as a buffer between him and the incident Ginger felt pretty secure and, in any case, he'd had all day to dream up plausible excuses. He reasoned that the best excuse would be the simplest one and with that in mind, he settled on a plan to tell the PO – if he ever asked him – that the stores people had told him to come back on the following day and that he was awaiting further instructions.

That was the plan but it was never executed. He didn't see that petty officer for several days and when they were in close proximity once more he appeared to have forgotten all about the episode. But, by then, Ginger had other things on his mind. Something of far more interest than dodging the quarterdeck PO: they had been told that the ship was going to Holland.

Maybe that kind of news was old hat to the ships company and nothing to even raise an eyebrow over but in the boys mess it was a different story. When the news was made official, the place was electric with excitement. It would be their first time to set foot on foreign soil; they were going abroad. They had been in the Navy for something well over a year and more like fifteen months. During all that time, apart from a day on the destroyer Obdurate just plodding around off Harwich and lately doing the same around Portland Bay, they had been nowhere and seen very little. Now they were heading for foreign shores

The buzz was Rotterdam. Excitement was in the air. The boys couldn't understand the complacency of the ships company but that couldn't dampen their enthusiasm. At last they were really going abroad. Even the normally depressing grey North Sea was shimmering blue and the sun was shining as they approached the Dutch coast. Magic was in the air.

The boys were called early to prepare for entering harbour, an evolution they had been told about but never had to perform before, and it was not long before the ships company were fallen in on the flight deck ready for the long trip up the river Waal.

Naturally all the boys had to fall in for entering harbour and, although it was a long way up the river and took quite a while, they didn't mind because it was a splendid vantage point from where to view the sights all the way from the sea and right into the maritime heart of Rotterdam.

Rotterdam was a long way inland and was situated at the end of a very busy waterway. It was one of the largest in Europe and probably the world, they were told. It was twenty miles from the sea and the trip up the river gave them plenty of time to see the sights. It was a lovely sunny day and not a bit cold, even with the forward motion of the ship as she headed for the city. In any case it was better than being one deck down and handling the ropes and hawsers required for berthing alongside.

Finally the big ship slid gently into the Holland–America Line section of the wall and immediately heaving lines snaked out to be followed by the ropes and hawsers that would grapple her alongside. Ginger marvelled at the coming alongside routine. It appeared to happen so effortlessly. He was intrigued by how such a big ship could be so graceful. It occurred to him that the Dutch people they had passed on the way in must have had similar thoughts. They must have been used to the commercial traffic that was constantly entering or leaving the big port but Implacable must have looked majestic as she slid slowly but purposely through the water.

Almost as the last line was secured so the gangways were slid into place. One was on the quarterdeck and another in the waist, in the centre of the ships side. Soon after, Ginger watched a party of Dutch naval officers come on board as, they were to learn, was the custom whenever a ship entered a foreign port. They were escorted straight to the wardroom to complete the welcoming formalities and undoubtedly sample some Royal Naval hospitality. Meanwhile the last finishing touches of sweeping, mopping and polishing were completed and soon after hands were piped to dinner.

After dinner leave was piped over the Tannoy and anyone not on duty was allowed ashore. Unlike Ganges, boys were permitted shore leave but it came to an end at 19.30 by which time they had to be back on board. Ginger was duty part of the watch so all he could do was to watch in envy as most of his messmates changed into a blue suit and raced for the gangway and the city.

They hadn't been gone very long before he was obliged to don a blue suit as well although, sadly, not for a run ashore. His blue suit came with the accessories of a white belt and a pair of gaiters. He had been lumbered with a security patrol of the upper hangar where the local merchants were displaying their trinkets and souvenirs for sale.

Why he had been singled out seemed rather strange, him a mere boy. What could he do to control hordes of ships company, all of whom were older and a lot worldlier wise than him? He was soon to learn the answer to that one and the answer was nothing. He had asked the duty PO that had assigned him to the task what he was there for, when they first arrived in the hangar and was told a lot of waffle about maintaining control and keeping the gangways clear or, in other words the duty PO didn't know either. Not that it mattered to him because a minute later he was gone and Ginger was on his own.

A look round the various stalls, although they were not stalls, they were just things laid out on a blanket on the deck, seemed to be the next order of business; partly out of curiosity because he had never seen the likes before, partly to be seen, although what effect that would have wasn't clear, and partly just to waste time until he could get out of there. As he approached the first stall, the vendor, an old man, leapt up eager to show him a bit of paper that he held in his hand. Ginger guessed that it would be his pass for permission to be there trading. He also thought that the old man wouldn't have got as far as the hangar if the pass wasn't genuine. He gave it a cursory look rather than draw attention to himself by not looking and gave the old trader a nod and waved him away. There was no way he was going to get mixed up with passes, genuine or not.

A few minutes later he saw a couple of ships company people grabbing things and hiding them under their coats while an accomplice held the old man's attention. He turned away swiftly; he didn't want another vendor to report him for not doing anything. He couldn't chase all three in any case and all he would do would be to make himself a marked man, so he wasn't about to get mixed up in that either.

He knew from the very start that he was serving no useful purpose up there in his blue suit and 'official' belt and gaiters, but that's what the Navy said had to be done and that's what he did. He didn't have to like it but to complain or, even worse, refuse, would have meant no run ashore in the coming days and quite possibly for many days after that. That petty officer wasn't there and no one had come to check up on him. He was all on his own with possibly as many as sixty or seventy people milling round. The only sensible answer was to adopt a low profile.

They had told him to wear a blue suit for the occasion but, to his way of thinking, a far better option would have been his 'green coat'. Although they all felt grown up and old hands now that Ganges was behind them, as far as anyone in authority was concerned he was a young lad and what do young lads know about patrols and crowd control, or whatever it was that he was meant to be doing. The old hand could be a vulnerable young lad when the occasion demanded. He wasn't too proud to wear that green coat when it suited him to do so.

He had been told that he would be relieved but after stand-easy came and went it looked as if he was there until the traders left but then, just as disappointment was turning to despair, his relief turned up. He didn't recognise the relief, he must have been an ordinary seaman from the ships company mess. He had gaiters but no belt. He said that he wanted Ginger's belt. Ginger was happy to give it to him. They met half way across the hangar deck and apart from those few words, and the handing over of the belt, Ginger was out of there and down that ladder to safety. If anybody complained about having trinkets nicked or got caught with their fingers in the pot, it didn't happen on his shift. He saw nothing and he knew nothing.

Back on the messdeck he had missed the cup of stand-easy tea but he was so relieved to have got away from that hangar that he didn't mind. Anyway it was almost teatime and a fresh brew. They had to change into a blue suit every day at 4 o'clock, so as he was already in one and there didn't seem much point in changing, he sat in the mess quietly waiting for teatime and his sticky bun.

That was his first time as an official; although he did have one incident at Ganges when he had to man a little sentry box just south of the wardroom, one evening in the dark. On that occasion no one had told him why he was there or what he was expected to do either, and just like this time there was no inquest after and the matter was never mentioned again. It was just the Navy being the Navy.

There was leave granted every afternoon while they were tied up alongside but they had to work hard during the forenoon to make up for it, particularly the boys. Everybody on board, it seemed, wanted a squad of boys to do the work. Boys were everywhere like ants, especially on the quarterdeck. That was where the official gangway was. That was the place that anyone coming aboard saw first. That was the place that was a continual hive of activity. That was the place that had to be immaculate. The brasswork shone, the paintwork glistened, the boards of the deck were so white they almost dazzled and it was all due to the boys. Boys whose only reward for all that work was to have to be back from shore leave at 19.30.

Ginger's duty, like all duties, carried over until midday the following day, and after he had helped with the washing up of the dinner plates and dishes in the mess he, like everyone else, was eager to be getting ashore.

It was a fair old walk out of the dock area and into the city and the boys hurried along so as not to miss too much of their short taste of freedom. They had been given a talk on Rotterdam as they made their way up the channel and across the North Sea. They learned that the city had been bombed almost flat a decade earlier during the height of the war and they were surprised by the cleanliness and newness everywhere. Perhaps, subconsciously, they were expecting to have to clamber over piles of rubble still. But everything looked brand new, as indeed it was. In the short space of not much more than a dozen years the inhabitants had worked miracles in getting the place rebuilt.

Once outside the docks the first thing they encountered was a wooden bridge over a canal. Across the other side the city opened up before them. Ginger's first impression of Rotterdam, before he even had time to marvel at the newness of the place, was the amount of bicycles to be seen. In fact, they had to wait at the bridge to allow cyclists across. There was so many of them that they were seven or eight abreast and took a few minutes to clear. As he ventured further into the city he noticed bicycles in little parks and stands all over the place. He wondered how they ever found their own cycle again.

Dark haired Taffy Dai was leading the way; Taffy was the chap who stopped Dereham's commandeering of the iron several months earlier. Dereham had been one of the first over the gangway the day before and, luckily, he wasn't with them on their jaunt.

A modern city now stood where demolished houses and shops and bomb blast holes had been but they were not particularly taken by the modern architecture, they were more interested in the brightly lit shop windows and the array of Dutch goods and souvenirs they displayed. Although they were in Holland he was surprised to see the amount of ornamental clogs that were for sale. They ranged from the very small, not much bigger than his thumb, right up to enormous ones that must have been made for Gulliver of *Gulliver's Travels* fame. He was even more surprised, indeed amazed, to see that many of the city folk still wore the traditional clogs whilst going about their everyday activities.

The contents of those shop windows were completely new to him and took him back to his early schooldays when he would stand and stare in awe at the toy shop windows of Norwich. In those days there was no chance of him acquiring anything however much he desired it and now, looking in those Rotterdam shop windows, he wished that he hadn't been quite as free with his money the previous week when they had been paid. He would have dearly liked to have bought a small pair of those ornamental clogs to give to his mother as a memento of his first trip abroad but, thanks to his over indulgence in goffas and chocolate, that was not to be and all he could do was to stand and stare at them.

Dai had a little money left and he bought himself, Ginger and their travelling companion a coca-cola each then after another tour of the part of the city they had already seen, the trio trooped back on board in time for supper. There was no point in hanging it out until the last minute before going back aboard. They had no money between them and to go back at 19.30 simply meant they would get nothing to eat until the morning. As much as they hated the idea of going back early, that was the sensible idea. They might be a bit miserable but at least they wouldn't be hungry.

After a few days alongside, they transferred to buoys out in mid river but that made no difference to Ginger, he didn't have any money and had no intention of going ashore again. What it did mean was that the motorboats were called into constant use. There were still stores to be brought aboard, officials to meet and greet and shore leave bodies to be ferried to and fro. Ginger was not asked to go back to the pinnace. Although the pinnace crew were friendly enough toward him, maybe they figured that they were just as well off without a boy under their feet and, in any case, he wouldn't be allowed to work late into the night for the last couple of runs of the liberty boat.

All too soon it was time to leave. It was not soon enough for Ginger. From the comfort of the boat deck or whilst working on the quarterdeck, he had been content to watch the commercial ships coming and going and people working away loading and unloading but all in all he was glad to be on the move.

They steamed out of the Waal river mouth, retracing their route down the English Channel but this time they went straight past Portland and up through the Irish Sea to Scotland.

It was on that voyage that Ginger made a discovery of his own. Despite being the quintessential 'grey man in a green coat' he had a propensity to let his mouth run away with him on occasion. He had been told so several times in the past and although he had taken notice, such occurrences usually happened on the spur of the moment and more often than not, catching him by surprise when his thoughts turned themselves into words and belched forth without warning. On that particular occasion those thoughts were aided and abetted by a not very pleasant demeanour brought about by having been woken out of a deep sleep.

In the lower hangar, at the back of the boys messdeck, there was a kind of a shed, not much more than a large tin box really but the interesting thing was that the roof of the shed didn't reach all the way to the deckhead above and there was a space of about four feet. Into this space were shoved spare seat cushions and other odd bits. The boys soon found that was a good place to pass away an hour or two, out of the ever-vigilant gaze of their mess petty officer. Mick Southern often made use of the facility and, on this particular evening, had crept in there for a snooze and had slept on into the night unnoticed.

During the night the lifebuoy sentry had reported that he thought something or someone had gone over the side, occasioning a full-scale alert. Lower deck was cleared and everyone was mustered in the upper hangar. The boys' mess muster position was on the port side, facing to starboard and near to the entrance door, but when Ginger arrived, later than everyone else, they were not in their usual position. It was dark in the hangar, to help with the night vision should they be required to go outside, and Ginger, still more than half asleep and not knowing what was going on was like a lost sheep as he looked for his mess position. All it took was for someone to say 'over here' but that was too easy and the entire ships company watched him stagger around.

Eventually the Chief Buffer had to add his two penn'orth but instead of shoving or pointing him in the right direction, he had to turn it into a major production. Three sides of a square were taken up by ships-company and the fourth was where the officers stood, with the buffer in front. Ginger copped his full wrath. Maybe it was an act to appease the officers and all he had to do was stand still and take it. But no, if the Buffer could shout unnecessarily then so could Ginger.

Everybody, except him apparently, was in a blue suit. Ginger was wearing the overalls he had laid out ready for the morning. This was a muster to ascertain if anyone had fallen over the side, what difference did it make what clothes anyone was wearing?

The Buffer was in full flow. If there was anybody in the water they could wait. Shades of Batchelor came flooding back. Ginger started off being afraid but the tirade went on so long that calmness came over him. That was replaced by frustration. If there was someone in need of help why was he standing there shouting? Frustration became anger as Ginger could listen to no more. Everything was wrong. It was even his fault that someone was missing although he was asleep at the time.

Quite out of character and having had the rebellion torn out of him at Ganges, Ginger stepped forward and right up to the Buffer's face. 'Oh, you forgot something,' he declared loudly. 'My shoes are dirty too!'

It was about then that he made his discovery: you do not answer back. You most certainly do not answer back in front of witnesses and under no circumstances in front of the entire ships company, including all the officers.

It was eventually discovered that no one had succumbed to a watery grave as Mick was winkled out of his hidey-hole and the ship resumed her course.

In the morning Mick received a fearsome dressing down and resolved to sleep in his hammock in future. Ginger was not so fortunate. He received three cuts for insubordination.

He had gone through Ganges without even the threat of cuts and now on a ship he had his first encounter. He wondered if that would be his last .... *or the first of many?*